FOLKTALES OF *Japan*

 *Folktales*
OF THE WORLD

GENERAL EDITOR : RICHARD M. DORSON

FOLKTALES OF
Japan

EDITED BY
Keigo Seki

TRANSLATED BY
ROBERT J. ADAMS

FOREWORD BY
RICHARD M. DORSON

THE UNIVERSITY OF CHICAGO PRESS

The tales in this volume have been selected
from *Nihon no Mukashi-banashi* (*Japanese
Folktales*), published by Iwanami Shoten,
Tokyo, in 1956–57, and have been translated
by Robert J. Adams
Library of Congress Catalog Card Number: 63-13071
The University of Chicago Press, Chicago 60637
Routledge & Kegan Paul, Ltd., London
© *1963 by The University of Chicago. All rights reserved. Published 1963*
Third impression 1969. Printed in the United States of America

Foreword

In Japan the scientific collection and study of folktales began a century later than in Europe. In 1812 Jacob and Wilhelm Grimm wrote down word-of-mouth tales from a German peasant woman, initiating a method of harvesting folk narratives which would be emulated in every country in Europe before the close of the nineteenth century. But it was not until 1910 that Kunio Yanagita, then a thirty-five-year-old inspector for the Japanese Ministry of Agriculture, first set down some oral stories from a farmer in his *Tono Monogatari* (*Stories from Tōno,* a district in Iwate-ken in northern Honshu), in the course of recording beliefs about village deities and seasonal customs.

Traditional tales had found their way into writing and into print as far back as the eighth century. Numerous folklore themes appear in the *Kojiki* (A.D. 712) and *Nihongi* (A.D. 720), and the international tale of "The titmouse who flies into the bear's ear and kills him" (Type 228 in the standard index of Aarne-Thompson) is recorded in the *Nihongi* as an actual event of the fourth century which occurred during the building of a tomb for Emperor Nintoku. Among literary collections, the *Konjaku Monogatari* of the twelfth century assembled in thirty-one volumes over a thousand narratives of various kinds—legends, wonder tales, fables, anecdotes. They came from Indian, Chinese, and Japanese sources, and many were drawn from oral tradition and help date the antiquity of tales heard today.

Western readers were introduced to *Tales of Old Japan* by Lord Redesdale in 1871, soon after the opening of Japan to the outside world. Among his translations of literary sketches and genre pieces, Redesdale (or A. B. Mitford, the name he used on

the title page), who was second secretary to the British legation
in Japan, included one section of "Fairy Tales" and another "Con-
cerning Certain Superstitions." These tales, written in a florid
Victorian English, were taken from little block-printed pamphlets
read by Japanese mothers to their children. "I think that their
quaintness is a sufficient apology for the following little children's
stories," Mitford wrote, with a naïveté equal to that he imputed
to his tales. Still he had happened onto a handful of genuine
mukashi-banashi (fairy tales) and *densetsu* (legendary tales),
even though at second hand. Fictions such as "The Crackling
Mountain" ("Kachi Kachi Mountain" in the present volume)
and believed accounts of demonic foxes and badgers are widely
known in Japanese villages. Such a publication can stand as a
pioneer venture for 1871—but curiously no work in English has
superseded it till the present collection, and students of international folktales have been compelled to cite Mitford. Numerous
children's editions of the same tired fairy tales written in the
customary precious manner and illustrated with the conventional
murky drawings have been issued for Japan as for other countries,
but these are valueless to the serious student of tales.

Lafcadio Hearn brought to American readers some sense of
Japanese legendry in such books as *Kwaidan* and *Glimpses of
Unfamiliar Japan,* published between 1894 and 1905. The priestly
traditions that attracted and haunted him catch the somber tones
of demonology and spiritism in Japanese village tales. But Hearn
wrote down these eerie legends, some told him by an acolyte,
others translated for him by his wife, in the mood of the mysteri-
ous East—exotic, occult, melancholic—rather than in the straight-
forward style of peasant storytellers. And much of the rural repertoire escaped him.

The task of properly investigating this repertoire rightfully
belonged to Japanese scholars, and Kunio Yanagita has given an
account of his efforts to locate folk narrators and to collect their
stories. Following his chance contact with the farmer Kizen Sasaki
in Iwate-ken, Yanagita turned his attention to deliberate plans
for capturing tales. Although the Aarne-Thompson *Types of the
Folk-Tale,* summarizing well-known European folktales in a
convenient catalogue, would not appear in Europe until 1928,

Yanagita knew the *Handbook of Folklore,* prepared by Charlotte
Burne for the English Folklore Society in 1913 and translated into
Japanese by Masao Oka in 1927 (*Minzokugaku Gairon*). He per-
ceived in its table of seventy-two tale plots a model for a Japanese
finding list. In order to discover representative samples of Japanese traditional stories, Yanagita issued from 1928 to 1944 a maga-
zine, *Tabi to Densetsu* (*Travels and Legends*), which solicited
descriptions of trips and scenes in the countryside along with the
tales told by country folk. As contributors began sending in local
traditions, their likenesses became apparent, and Yanagita was
able to identify common patterns. Accordingly he conceived the
idea of publishing a guidebook which could be used both to
exemplify and to elicit Japanese folktales. This unusual volume,
Mukashi-banashi Saishu Techo (*A Guide for Collecting Folk
Tales*), distributed in 1936, had bald summaries of one hundred *mukashi-banashi* on the right-hand page, and blank sheets
on the left-hand side. Readers could learn from the introduction
and the synopses the nature of oral tales and write down their
own variations on the blank pages. This ingenious idea failed to
produce expected results because the recipients found stories, even
in outline, of such interest that they retained the books for their
own shelves. Another abortive plan was the scholarly journal devoted entirely to folktales, *Mukashi-banashi Kenkyū,* which included collectors' reports, comparative studies, and translations of
treatises by Western folklorists, but it lasted only two years, from
1935 to 1937, failing for lack of enough consistent and trustworthy
contributors.

Yet the endeavors of Yanagita were now attracting interest from
cultural nationalists, and in 1940 the Japan Broadcasting Association, engaged in a fervent campaign to promote Japanese culture,
requested him to make a special study of indigenous folktales and
legends. The Association bore a considerable part of the expense
involved in mobilizing Japanese folklorists and collectors for this
task and, after the war, published the final selections, as prepared
by Kunio Yanagita, under the titles *Nihon Mukashi-banashi Meii*
(*An Index of Japanese Folktales*) in 1948 and *Nihon Densetsu
Meii* (*An Index of Japanese Legends*) in 1950.

In the ambitious collecting campaign which began with the

handbook and reached a climax with the indexes, Yanagita, with associates such as Keigo Seki, sought out elderly narrators of little education as the persons most likely to have escaped the influence of literary sources. In most cases they were rice farmers, deep-sea fishermen, and their wives, resident in remote villages. Half a dozen of these venerable villagers recounted more than a hundred stories apiece to the collectors.

In the end the most effective means of unearthing and printing folktales proved to be local fieldwork of this sort, undertaken by individuals and societies now acquainted with the concepts and techniques of folklore research. For instance, the farmer from Iwate-ken, Kizen Sasaki, whom Yanagita had exhaustively inter-rogated in 1910 on all aspects of the regional folk life in Tōno, began to write down his own and his neighbors' repertoire and, in *Kikimi Sōshi* (*The Listening Ear Story Book,* 1931), presented what Yanagita has called the greatest folktale collection of Japan. From the collecting activities thus stimulated by his own efforts, Yanagita was able to edit a series of thirteen regional volumes, *Zenkoku Mukashi-banashi Kiroku* (*Records of Folktales*), pub-lished from 1942 to 1944 and covering an area from Sado Island in the northeast to Koshiki Island in the southwest. The organiza-tion of study and research groups, such as Minzoku Gakkai (The Society for Folklore Studies), initiated in 1935, and the Minzoku-gaku Kenkyusho (The Folklore Research Institute), founded by Yanagita in 1948, gave further impetus to fieldwork, and by 1950 the Institute had check-listed some 20,000 folktales set down from oral tradition.

With a national storehouse of narrative traditions now plainly visible, Yanagita turned his attention to the problem of arranging them in an orderly way. His collector's handbook, *Mukashi-banashi Saishu Techo,* had already identified the most popular tale types, and Yanagita retained their order in the *Nihon Mukashi-banashi Meii,* a much more extensive work running to more than 800 pages. He now printed full rather than abbreviated examples and furnished references to local versions known throughout the country. In the first part of the book, "Complete Folktales," Yanagita included the well-structured fictions of won-der and adventure such as the Grimm brothers had found, and these he grouped according to their prominent themes. Thus in the category, "Caring for Unusual Children," would fall the Japanese tale most frequently translated into English in children's books, Momotaro, the Peach Boy, the child prodigy born from a peach pit. Under "Derived Folktales" are included briefer and less formal narratives—supernatural experiences, jokes and anecdotes, and the fictions in which animal and plant characters rather than human beings act the chief roles. Some of these latter forms verged on the legendary or believed tradition, but Yanagita carefully maintained the distinction between them, pointing out the much looser structure of the legend as well as its link with an "immovable evidence" or landmark.

The investigation of folk narrative used only a portion of Yanagita's energies as he explored the whole range of Japanese folk culture and, until his death on August 8, 1962, he encouraged younger disciples to pursue their own specialties. One such assistant was Keigo Seki, born in 1899 in Nagasaki-ken, where he heard old tales from his mother, which he later included in his field collection of 1935, *Shimabara Hantō Minwa Shū (Folktales from Shimabara Peninsula)*. After graduating in 1924 from Tokyo Gakugei Daigaku, whose faculty he subsequently joined as a lecturer in sociology, Seki worked with Yanagita in preparing the *Mukashi-banashi Saishu Techo* in 1936 and thenceforth devoted himself exclusively to the folktale. In 1940 he translated into Japanese the celebrated work of the Finnish folklorist Karl Krohn, *Die folkloristische Arbeitsmethode,* published in Oslo in 1926, which first systematized the principles of comparative folklore study (*Minzokugaku Hoho-ron* [Tokyo, 1940]). Such a paper as Seki's "The Spool of Thread: A Subtype of the Japanese Serpent-Bridegroom Tale" (*Studies in Japanese Folklore,* ed. R. M. Dorson [Bloomington, Indiana, 1963]) demonstrates his grasp of the Finnish method of comparing variant texts to establish regional subforms of a folktale and chart their travels in time and space.

For his major task Seki turned to a reclassification of the thousands of folktales which had accumulated in printed collections from 1910 to 1940. The *Nihon Mukashi-banashi Shusei (A Classification and Catalogue of Japanese Folktales)* appeared in six volumes, divided into three parts, between 1950 and 1958. Seki

did not radically depart from Yanagita's scheme but considerably
expanded, rearranged, and subdivided the national stock of oral
narratives.

In this massive index and anthology, Seki provides a sample
text for each of the over six hundred types, with a commentary
to each text giving its regional distribution, abstracts of the variants, and their places of publication. Some tales are found in over
a hundred examples. In his comparative notes Seki cites Japanese
literary classics and Asiatic and European collections. The main
differences between the Yanagita and the Seki indexes appear in
the enlargement and subdivision by Seki of the sections on animal
and bird tales and humorous stories, which Yanagita had regarded
as secondary forms. Some of the categories of well-known tale
cycles, such as those about the good old man and the bad old
man who lived next to each other ("Old Men Neighbors"), or
of stepchildren, lucky finders of treasure, and helpful animals,
appear in both registers.

As a complementary work to the *Shusei,* which was intended
primarily for reference, Seki edited three handy volumes in 1956
and 1957 containing a total of 240 folktales, under the title
Nihon no Mukashi-banashi. It is from this edition, representing
the by now well-established canon of Japanese traditional tales,
that the present selection is taken.

In the final volume of the *Shusei,* Seki provided an extensive
type-index (pp. 823–927), *Nihon Mukashi-banashi no Kata (Forms
of the Japanese Folktale),* in which he further refined his classification. This index is in effect a separate work (and is being sepa-
rately translated and published in English). Unlike the *Shusei,*
the *Kata* contains no full text of any tale but rather a composite
abstract formed from an examination of all the known variants.
This abstract is the type and receives a number. In the *Shusei*
the variants had been listed and synopsized, following the one
representative text. Now in the *Kata,* Seki constructed synthetic
or archetypal texts for 470 types, considerably reducing the number in the *Shusei* proper. The *Kata* therefore conforms to the
plan of the European tale-type index of Aarne-Thompson, save
that it is a national not an international index. As compared with
the *Shusei* and its thirty sections, the *Kata* has eighteen, eliminat-

ing the divisions based on single tales and further sharpening the categories. In a table of the section headings, Seki lists the number of texts analyzed for each theme and the percentage for each group in relation to the whole body of over ten thousand tales collected and classified.

The impression should not be conveyed that Japanese folklore research has moved in a smooth ascent from the labors of collecting to those of classification and now is ready for theoretical and comparative analyses. If in the main this development has taken place, the three endeavors have overlapped each other. Intensive local collecting continues with increasing profit. For example, a school principal, Kenichi Mizusawa, living in Niigata-ken, the "snow country" of northwestern Honshu, published in 1957 and 1958 five volumes of folktales he had gathered in the area, sometimes in remote villages he reached by ski. His students often led him to excellent narrators in the persons of their parents and grandparents. One storyteller alone furnished the materials for a whole book, with 122 narratives. Each year sees the known store of Japanese folktales enlarged.

How many of these folktales are international in currency and how many seem to be peculiarly Japanese? A student trained first under Yanagita and then under Stith Thompson at Indiana University qualified herself to answer this question. For her doctoral dissertation in 1955, Hiroko Ikeda constructed "A Type and Motif Index of Japanese Folk-Literature," analyzing some 2,894 folktales in her quest for European counterparts. Ikeda relied heavily on the *Shusei* for her references to oral folktales but also found folktale plots worming their way into Buddhist sermons, local legends, literary classics, dramatic performances, traditional history, and the jokes of city storytellers. On the basis of a close comparison with the Aarne-Thompson index of European tales, Ikeda concluded that some 80 per cent of Japanese folktales matched the Aarne-Thompson types. The remainder circulated exclusively in east Asia, or the circum-Pacific area, or were confined to Japan because of their special word-plays or demon characters. Ikeda's tally seems high and is reached by a certain amount of persuasion, squeezing recalcitrant plots into the Aarne-Thompson slots. Such a tale as "Kachi Kachi Mountain" (Nos.

3a and 3b in this volume), found in eighty-eight variants through-out Japan, is composed of a number of incidents, one of which may be associated with Type 43, "The Bear Builds a House of Wood, the Fox of Ice"; but the story outline has no real parallel outside Japan, and indeed Seki gives it a separate section in the *Shusei*. In the *Kata*, the highest percentage of any tale cycle (9.14%) is concerned with conflicts between neighbors known as the good old man and the bad old man, a theme rare in Europe.

Nevertheless, some surprising matches can be found between highly Japanized oral tales and common Western folktales and even to modern American jokes. In the summer of 1961 the wife of a colleague of mine, who possesses the gift of rattling off jokes in an endless flow, told the following at a party.

> A white man traveling on a bus down south felt a strong need to relieve himself. The bus stopped for engine repairs along a country road in the middle of nowhere; not a house, tree, or even a bush was in sight. The man with the full bladder wondered what to do. Then off in the distance he saw a Negro digging in the ground. He walked over to him, pondering how he could take advantage so the people in the bus wouldn't see him. Stepping behind the colored man, he started up a conversation. "Well, tell me, what's your name?" "Well, boss, my name is Ezekiel." "And say, tell me, do you live here?" "Well yes, boss, I live here, over yonder ways." "Well now, what do you grow here in this country?" "Well, boss, a little bit of this and that." "Are you married?" "Yes, boss, I'se married." "Do you have any children?" "Yes, boss." "How many?" "Well, I'se got twelve." "What are their names?" "Well there's Amanda, and there's Samuel, and then there's Moses, and then there's Jeremiah, and there's Sarah Jones, and there's Peter—and say, boss, is you peein' on me?"

This story may not amuse some listeners or readers, but it does represent contemporary American jesting. My friend heard it from her twin sister who lives in Ft. Lauderdale, Florida, who in turn heard it from her husband. This is basically the same tale as No. 61 in the following pages, "There's No Deity There," where the incident is told about a Buddhist priest and his acolyte. The acolyte is faced with the same problem as our southern traveler, but is deterred from relieving himself on the ground because, as the priest explains, it is holy and dedicated to a *kami* (deity). Finally the acolyte lets go on the priest's head, because there was no *kami* there. In Japanese the same word stands for deity and hair; hence a clever pun has capped the relation. This Japanese version is thoroughly rooted in *minkan shinko,* or Japanese folk belief. *Kami* is a primary concept of Shintoism, and semi-divinities known as *kami* are attached to the house, the latrine, the yard; the presence of a *kami* in the ground under the acolyte fully supported the priest's restraining action with the strongest possible cultural sanction. Paradoxically, in Japan the practice of public urination causes no offense, while in the United States the social mores make such an act disgusting; hence the difficulty of our bus-rider. The presence of the Buddhist priest with his unshaven poll and the linguistic play afforded by *kami* further rationalize the jest in Japanese terms.

This illustration points to a central quality in the *mukashi-banashi* which distinguishes them from the household tales of Europe. The *mukashi-banashi,* or once-upon-a-time story, is close to the *densetsu,* or legend, which is told as an actual if extraordinary occurrence. Frequently, the same plot outline appears in both forms. While the vestiges of supernatural and magical beliefs can plainly be seen in the *Kinder- und Hausmärchen,* their hearers do not accept the malice of witches and ogres or the jealousies of talking animals as real. In the Japanese tales, however, the sense of fiction and fantasy is much less pronounced. Modern Japan emerged only with the Meiji Restoration of 1868, and her traditions are tenaciously rooted in a living folk culture. The Japanese fox inhabits a different universe from the fox of Europe, for he is no animal but a demon, a transformer, and a degenerated deity, once indeed the special messenger of Inari, god of the rice fields. And so with the other creatures, like the monkey and the badger and the serpent, who are still thought of in the village mind as fallen divinities. The stories of supernatural husbands and wives and of ogres like the *oni* belong not to a children's realm of fairyland but to a danger-laden adult world where *kami* descend from the heavens and emerge from the mountains and swamps, whose essence, indeed, they embody. As the legends are close to rituals and beliefs still prevalent in the villages and even the cities, so are the fictions close to the legends. Within the *mukashi-banashi* are imbedded the codes and creeds that Japanese folk have lived by since the dawn of their history.

Bibliographical details on Japanese folklore may be found in my essay, "Bridges between Japanese and American Folklorists," in *Studies in Japanese Folklore* (Bloomington, Ind., 1961), pp. 3–49.

RICHARD M. DORSON

Translator's Note

Because of centuries of relative isolation from the rest of the world, Japanese culture has produced phenomena completely unfamiliar to Western readers. This fact poses difficulties to the translator which are not easily solved. To help in understanding the tales a note of explanation on the solution of some of these problems is given here.

An attempt has been made to translate as literally as possible, consistent with clear, idiomatic English. Terms for which there are no English equivalents have been transliterated and explained either in the text, in the notes, or in the glossary. Those items of food, wearing apparel, tools, units of measure and monetary units, and so on, which are generally unfamiliar to Western readers have been transliterated and explained.

Suffixes of address used in the Japanese have been retained since the relationship of the characters in a tale is very often expressed in the degree of either familiarity or respect revealed by the choice of these suffixes.

The Japanese language is rich in onomatopoeia; an attempt has been made to retain the flavor of the original by transliterating as many of these expressions as possible.

Introductory and closing phrases of most Japanese tales are more or less stylized. The usual opening phrase, *mukashi,* or *mukashi mukashi,* has been translated as "long ago" or "long, long ago." Where a story does not open with *mukashi,* it may begin with the phrase, *aru tokoro ni,* translated as "in a certain place."

Closing phrases are more varied and in some cases so highly stylized that they have little direct bearing on the story. In view of this fact they have been transliterated and explained either in the notes or in the glossary.

The orthography used here in reducing Japanese script to the Latin alphabet is the Hepburn system. The pronounciation of Japanese is similar to Italian; the five vowel sounds are not glided but may be lengthened. Each syllable of a word is given equal stress; accent is in quality of pitch rather than stress.

The tales translated here were chosen from a selection made by Professor Keigo Seki, noted Japanese folklorist and disciple of the founder of the scientific study of folklore in Japan, Kunio Yanagita. Professor Seki selected the best representative examples of some 240 stories from a total of over 15,000 tales and versions collected throughout Japan by many individual folklorists and collectors. These 240 tales were published in a three-volume edition, *Nihon no Mukashi-banashi* (*Japanese Folktales* [Tokyo: Iwanami Shoten, 1956–57]). The versions chosen were given as collected from the informant, the only change being the rendering of dialect expressions into standard Japanese, a change necessitated by the often nearly total unintelligibility of dialect Japanese to the average reader.

I have selected sixty-three tales from those chosen by Professor Seki. My selection was based largely on the popularity of each tale as represented by its distribution in Japan given by Professor Seki in his *Nihon Mukashi-banashi Shusei* (*A Classification and Catalogue of Japanese Folktales*) and by Hiroko Ikeda in her *A Type and Motif Index of Japanese Folk-Literature*. I have attempted to give a representative sample of the best-known Japanese tales, including tales about animals, tales of the supernatural, and jokes and anecdotes.

In assigning Aarne-Thompson tale-type numbers, I have relied heavily on Ikeda's research. The Kata numbers are those assigned to the tales by Professor Seki in his *Nihon Mukashi-banashi no Kata*. I have assigned the majority of the Motif-Index numbers appended to the tales.

While I have received help from many sources, I wish to give particular acknowledgment to my wife, Yasuko, without whose patient and unstinting help this translation would not have been possible.

ROBERT J. ADAMS

Introduction

It was not until the 1920's that the serious collecting of folk-tales for the purpose of academic research began in Japan. Though very few tales had been collected up to that time, the constant and energetic efforts of local folklorists since then have enabled them to collect over 15,000 tales, which are now available for research work. While these laborious and unremitting collecting efforts continue, more than half of Japan remains unexplored by the folklorist. Field investigation has been pursued in remote villages and islands, and aged persons who are not blessed with books or periodicals have been selected as informants. A professional class of storyteller did not exist in these regions, but many storytellers can be located among the farmers and fishermen. The traditional forms of old tales are well preserved throughout the village society.

According to their thematic resemblances, all the tales available can be classified into three great groups. The percentage of tales in each form is as follows.

Animal Tales	13 per cent
Ordinary Tales	50 per cent
Jokes and Anecdotes	37 per cent

They are also classified into some six hundred tale types and the percentage of types in each grouping is as follows.

Animal Tales	13 per cent
Ordinary Tales	33 per cent
Jokes and Anecdotes	54 per cent

Some of the tales are found in over one hundred variants, while others have only two or three variants and therefore hardly qualify as distinct tale types. My edition of *Nihon no Mukashi-*

banashi (Japanese Folktales, 3 vols.), written with the intention of stimulating the collection and research of Japanese folktales, includes only texts which satisfy the following requirements.

1. Tales with definite forms and coherent plots that have been recorded word for word.
2. Tales whose informants, locations, and dates of collection are identifiable.
3. Tales that are representative versions of each tale type.
4. Tales that are widely distributed and told very often.
5. Tales representing all parts of Japan.

The original Japanese collection contained 240 items. In this English edition 63 tales have been chosen, over half of which are correlated with the Aarne-Thompson Tale-Type Index.

To Robert J. Adams I wish to express my appreciation for an excellent translation and for his preparation of the headnotes to the tales.

KEIGO SEKI

Contents

I. ANIMAL TALES

1	The Fish Thief	3
2	The Hare, Badger, Monkey, and Otter	4
3a	Kachi Kachi Mountain	6
3b	The Rabbit and the Bear	9
4	The Quail and the Badger	14
5	The Monkey and the Crab	15
6	The Monkey and the Pheasant	16
7	The Wolf's Reward	20
8	The Greedy Hawk	22
9	The Whale and the Sea Slug	23
10	The Cat and the Crab	25
11	The Monkey's Liver	25
12	The Rain Leak in an Old House	27
13	The Mole's Bridegroom	29
14	An Endless Story	30

II. OGRES

15	Shippei Taro	33
16	The *Oni*'s Laughter	36
17	Momotaro, The Peach Boy	40

18   The Dirt Boy   43
19   The Three Lucky Charms   47
20   The *Oni* and the Three Children   51
21   The Golden Chain from Heaven   54
22   The Swamp *Nushi's* Messenger   57

III. SUPERNATURAL HUSBANDS OR WIVES

23   The Woman Who Came Down from Heaven   63
24   The Fire Boy   70
25   The Crane Wife   77
26   The Snow Wife   81
27   The Snail *Choja*   82
28   Little One Inch   90
29   The White Bird Sister   92
30   The Girl without Arms   98

IV. KINDNESS REWARDED AND
     EVIL PUNISHED

31   The Good Fortune Kettle   107
32   Urashima Taro   111
33   The Tongue-cut Sparrow   115
34   The Old Man Who Cut Bamboo   118
35   The Old Man Who Made Flowers Bloom   120
36   The Old Men Who Had Wens   126
37   The Monkeys' Jizo-*sama*   128
38   Benizara and Kakezara   130
39   The Salt-Grinding Millstones   134
40   The Magic Ear   139
41   The *Choja* Who Became a Monkey   142
42   The Skeleton's Song   145

V. GOOD FORTUNE

43 The Charcoal Burner *Choja* 151

44 Luck from Heaven and Luck from the Earth 155

45 The Man Who Bought a Dream 157

46 The Advice That Cost a Thousand *Ryo* 160

VI. CLEVERNESS AND STUPIDITY

47 The Monkey Bridegroom 167

48 The Wife's Portrait 170

49 The Golden Eggplant 173

50 The Bundles of Straw and the King's Son 176

51 The Boy Who Told Tall Tales 179

52 A Tall Tale Contest 181

53 The Mountain Where Old People Were Abandoned 183

54 The Three Year Sleeping Boy 186

55 The Nun as Judge 188

56 The Clever Lord 189

57 The Hawk Fledgling 190

58 Stinginess 192

59 It's Been Well Used 192

60 The Pillow 193

61 There's No Deity There 194

62 The Sweet *Mochi*'s Parents 195

63 Bedding in One's Ear 197

Glossary 199

Bibliography 203

Index of Motifs 205

Index of Tale Types 207

Index of Kata Numbers 209

General Index 213

Part I
Animal Tales

.1. The Fish Thief

This tale is a combination of Type 1, The Theft of Fish, and Type 2, The Tail Fisher. Kata No. 31, "The Fish Thief." Collected in Tomioka-mura, Iruma-gun, Saitama-ken, from a neighbor of the collector, Kikue Arai.

The variant given here forms the first two tales of the cycle known as Reynard the Fox. This was the first series of tales to be given an intensive study by the famous Finnish folklorist, Kaarle Krohn. Thompson, p. 220, cites Krohn's conclusion that the cycle developed in the folk tradition of northern Europe. If this assumption is true, the tale presents an interesting problem in the diffusion of folktales. It has an important position in Japanese oral tradition, with sixty-eight versions recorded, but it has not been extensively reported in India, and not at all in China. Thompson and Roberts, p. 21, list eight variants of Type 1 and two of Type 2. Krohn had none of the Japanese variants available when he made his study in 1889; if a review of the cycle were to be made in the light of variants made available in the past seventy-five years, such a study might help to clarify some of the puzzling relationships between European and Japanese folk tradition.

• IT WAS A cold winter's day. A fisherman had caught a number of fish through a hole in the ice. He had loaded them on his sled and was returning home. A fox saw them, and since he liked fish so much, and was also very hungry, he determined to get some of the fish.

He ran ahead of the sled a short way, then lay down in the road as though he were dead. The fisherman came along and, wanting a fox skin to make a cap with, picked up the fox, supposing it to be dead. He threw it on the sled and drove on home with his load of fish.

When the fisherman wasn't looking, the fox took one of the fish and replaced it with a stone so that the fisherman would not notice the load's becoming lighter. He then jumped off and ran into the forest.

As he was in the forest eating the fish, a bear came by. "Where did you get the fish?" he asked.

"I caught it."

"I'd like to catch a fish like that."

"Well, I'll tell you the secret of catching fish," said the fox. "You go on down this trail and you'll come to a river. The river is frozen over, but there is a round hole in the ice. You stick your tail down the hole and leave it a while. The fish will come and grab hold of it; then you can haul up your tail along with the fish and so you will have caught one."

The bear happily ran off and found the hole in the ice. He stuck his tail in. He waited patiently for a fish to take hold of it. Finally he felt as though something had fastened onto it. "That must be a big fish which has grabbed my tail," he cried, "ah, what a feast I'll have!" and he gave his tail a jerk. Feeling something break, he fell face forward and rolled over on the ice. Wondering what could have happened, he looked around and saw his tail, torn off at the roots and stuck fast in the ice.

•2• *The Hare, Badger, Monkey, and Otter*

Type 3, Sham Blood and Brains. Kata No. 34A, "The Badger, the Rabbit, and the Otter." Collected in Shimizu-mura, Agawa-gun, Kochi-ken, from Mitsu Kawauchi.

The motif of feigning sickness in order to escape exposure as a cheat, K473, "Sham blood and brains," forms the third tale in the cycle of Reynard the Fox, mentioned in the note to tale No. 1, above.

In Japanese, as in American Negro tradition, the hare or rabbit often plays the role of trickster in animal tales. This tale is well known in Japan; forty versions have been recorded.

• LONG AGO in a certain place there was a salt peddler named Chobei. One day he had bought some salt, some beans, a water wheel, and a straw mat, and as he was going along he became tired, so he sat down to rest. Nearby were a hare, a badger, a monkey, and an otter.

The hare said to the others, "If I run by in front of him, pretending to be lame, Chobei will be sure to try to catch me; so while he is running after me, you three take his basket of stuff and run off with it."

The hare ran in front of Chobei, pretending to be lame. Sure enough, just as he had expected, Chobei grabbed his carrying pole and ran after the hare. While he was gone, the other three animals took his basket and dragged it away. Finally the hare escaped from him, and Chobei went back to where he had left his stuff, but the basket was not there. Angrily he took his carrying pole and disappeared.

The four animals gathered together and began to divide the things in the basket. "Because the otter dives into the river to catch crabs, we will give him the salt. He can put it on the crabs, and they will be delicious," said the hare, and so they gave the otter the salt.

"You sleep on the rocks at night, monkey-*dono;* so if you take this mat and sleep on it, you will be very comfortable," said the hare, and they gave the mat to the monkey.

"Badger-*dono,* you always sleep in your burrow; so if you take this and put it in the entrance of your hole, you can watch it spin around in the air as you lie in bed. That will be really interesting!" said the hare, and so they gave the badger the water wheel.

"There is nothing left for me but the beans, so I'll take them," said the hare. In this way the hare got the beans; then all four went their separate ways.

The otter immediately went to the river to catch some crabs, but when he dove into the water with the salt it soon dissolved and disappeared. The badger stayed awake all night, waiting for the water wheel to spin around, but it didn't move a bit. The otter and the badger became very angry and went to see the monkey. The monkey had laid out the mat on the rocks and tried to sleep on it but he had slipped off and bruised his buttocks.

The three of them, filled with anger, went to the hare's place.

The hare had been eating the beans and sticking the skins in his navel, eating some more and sticking the skins in his navel, and when the three animals came he said: "You all look angry too. Here I have eaten these beans, and look at what has come out of my navel. Oh, it hurts so badly I can hardly stand it!"

"Well, everybody has the same trouble!" said the others.

It is said that it is from that time that the monkey's buttocks became slick and bald, and it is for just that reason that they now shine so.

**· 3a, 3b ·   Kachi Kachi Mountain and
          The Rabbit and the Bear**

This tale-cycle, known in Japan in some eighty-eight versions, resembles the cycle of Reynard the Fox in Europe. Motifs may be added or may drop out in a variety of ways but the general outline of the tale remains constant. The two parts of the tale given here as "Kachi Kachi Mountain" and "The Rabbit and the Bear" are sometimes told as independent tales but are more often combined. The badger is almost always featured in the first half of the tale; in the second half, where revenge is taken, his part may be played by the bear. The rabbit is usually the one who brings revenge.

Type 43, The Bear Builds a House of Wood, the Fox of Ice, is similar to one of the incidents in this tale. The tale is shown in the Kata as No. 72B, "Kachi Kachi Mountain," and 73B, "The Rabbit and the Bear." The first part was collected in Saraki-mura, Waga-gun, Iwate-ken, from Kura Hirano, and the latter part in Iwate-gun, Iwate-ken.

Kachi Kachi is onomatopoeia from the scratch, scratch sound of iron on flint in making fire and also from the crackle of a burning fire.

Slapping one's buttocks is a rude gesture equivalent to the Western gesture of thumbing one's nose.

Kachi *birds and* bo-o *birds are non-existent; the names are invented here by the rabbit to explain the sounds he was making.*

• THIS HAPPENED long ago. There once lived an old man and his wife. One day the old man went to hoe his field on the mountain. An evil badger came and sat on the old man's resting stone. He called out insultingly,

> Old man, you're hoeing crooked on the right,
> Old man, you're hoeing crooked on the left.

"You worthless badger, all you do is bother people!" cried the old man and ran after the badger with his hoe.

"Look out, old man, you'll fall over backward on your rump," jeered the badger and ran off into the mountains, all the while slapping his buttocks [to show contempt for the old man].

The next day when the old man went to the mountain field to hoe, the badger again came to bother him. He called out, "Old man, you're hoeing crooked on the right."

"I'll have to do something about this," thought the old man to himself, and so the next day he brought some birdlime and thoroughly smeared the resting rock with it. That day the badger came again. Unaware that anything was there, he sat down on the resting stone.

> The seed you're sowing, old man,
> A thousand seeds will become just one.
> When evening comes,
> All will disappear,

he called out as he watched the old man sowing grain.

"What! Have you come again today, you badger! You're nothing but a worthless rascal," cried the old man. He grabbed up a handful of wisteria vines and ran after the badger. The badger tried to escape but was stuck fast in the birdlime. No matter how he tried, it was no use.

> The badger's rump has put out roots;
> When evening comes,
> We shall feast on badger soup,

cried the old man as he bound the wisteria vines around and around the badger and carried him home.

"Old lady, old lady, please cook some badger soup for this evening," he said, hanging the badger by the door post.

The old woman was out in the yard making flour, and the badger called from the doorway, "How much flour are you making, grandmother?"

"Three mortars full and a stack of three tubs full," she replied.

"With all that work, I feel sorry for you, but I'll help you do it, if you'll loosen up these vines just a little," said the badger.

"No, the old man would be angry," she said.

"Why should he be angry? After we're finished with the flour, you can hang me back up again," and the badger continued to bother her until the goodhearted old lady agreed to untie him.

"Now, grandmother, I'll grind the flour and you can help me," said the badger. Pretending to pound the mortar, he hit the old woman on the head as hard as he could. He hit her such a blow that she died. He skinned her and covered himself with her skin. Then he made her into soup and waited for the old man to return home.

When evening came the old man returned from the mountains and called, "Old lady, old lady, do you have the badger broth done yet?"

"Ah, here you are, old man. You're late, aren't you? The badger soup is done; please have some." And the badger, disguised as the old lady, offered the old man some of the soup he had made from the old woman.

"Ah, this should be delicious," cried the old man, but when he tried a mouthful, it had a strange, unfamiliar taste. "This is surely strange-tasting badger soup," said the old man, cocking his head to one side.

"When I was boiling the badger, he broke wind, and the soup tastes of that," explained the badger.

"Well, even at that, it is delicious, delicious," said the old man, and he ate three bowls of it.

After the old man had finished, the badger cried,

Here I've pulled the horse's rear teeth!
Isn't it strange to eat your wife in soup?

Pulling off the skin of the old lady, he ran *bonbori bonbori*, humpity-hump off into the mountains.

"Oh, how pitiful! Ah, ah, I was made to eat my wife. Oh, oh," the old man wept bitterly. Just then a rabbit came softly up to the old man. "What are you crying so about, grandfather?" he asked.

"Listen carefully and I'll tell you what happened," said the old man. Sobbing, he told the rabbit how the badger had come from the mountains, had killed the old woman, and had made her into soup, and how he had been made to eat it.

"You needn't cry any more, old man," said the rabbit, "I'll get revenge for you," and so he restored the old man's good spirits.

• THE RABBIT and the bear met in a certain place and decided to go to the mountains to gather firewood. They both put on straw raincapes and fastened some rope to their belts, then set off for the mountains.

Now the bear was rather stupid, but the rabbit was very clever. Before they had reached the mountains the rabbit was already crying, "Oh, such hard work, such hard work."

When they got to the mountains they busily began chopping down trees, *gari gari*. The bear was the stronger, and so he cut a lot of trees while the rabbit cut only a few. When they loaded the wood on their backs the bear took a lot, but the rabbit took only a little bit; then he stayed behind and cried, "Oh, it's too heavy, it's too heavy," and refused to walk a step.

"Rabbit-*dono*, rabbit-*dono*, you are certainly weak. Why see the load I have, and I can walk all right," said the bear. But no matter what, the rabbit refused to carry his load a single step.

"All right then, if it is so heavy for you, give me half of it," said the bear and took half of the rabbit's load of wood. Then they set off for home.

After they had gone a little way the rabbit again cried out,

"Oh, it's too heavy, it's too heavy," and refused to go further. "Rabbit-*dono*, rabbit-*dono*, what's the matter. If it is so very heavy, give me all of it." And the bear took all the wood the rabbit had and added it to his own load; then they set off again.

Even at that, after they had gone a ways further, the rabbit again cried out, "Oh, it's too hard, it's too hard," and refused to go further. "Well, if it is as hard as that, I'll carry you too," and so the bear walked along, carrying the rabbit on his back.

The rabbit, up on the bear's back, took out his fire-starting stone and *kachiri kachiri*, began to strike fire. "Rabbit-*dono*, rabbit-*dono*, what is that sound I hear up there on my back?" asked the bear.

"Oh that is the voice of the *kachi* bird on *Kachiri* Mountain," answered the rabbit, as if it were nothing unusual.

Next the rabbit began to blow on the fire, *bo-o bo-o*. "Rabbit-*dono*, rabbit-*dono*, what is that sound, *bo-o bo-o?*" asked the bear.

"Oh, that is the *bo-o bo-o* bird on *Bo-o Bo-o* Mountain," replied the rabbit. Then he jumped off the bear's back and ran away.

The fire on the bear's back began to get hot, and it was only then that he realized that he had been fooled by the rabbit.

The bear, his back covered with great burns, went groaning along until he had crossed the mountain, and there he saw the rabbit cutting wisteria vines. "Rabbit-*dono*, rabbit-*dono*, you played a mean trick on me just now, and I got badly burned."

The rabbit, looking as though he knew absolutely nothing about it, said, "That was the rabbit on the other mountain, the one on the other mountain. I am the Wisteria Mountain rabbit, the Wisteria Mountain rabbit, I know nothing about it."

The bear thought that the rabbit must be right, and he asked, "By the way, rabbit-*dono*, what are you cutting the wisteria vines for?"

"Oh, the weather is so nice today I thought I'd play in the sun a while, and so I am cutting these vines," replied the rabbit.

"That looks interesting," said the bear, "how about letting me join you?" So the two agreed to play together, and they cut a lot of wisteria vines. "Now, how do we play with these?" asked the bear.

"It's fun to go up to the top of the mountain, bind up one's hands and feet, then roll over and over down the mountain," said the rabbit.

"Oh, it must be!" said the bear, and they decided to let the bear go first. The two of them went up to the top of the mountain, and the rabbit tied up the bear's hands and feet.

"There, this is going to be really interesting; just roll a little and see," said the rabbit. "This will be fun," thought the bear. But when he started off he bumped into a tree here and fell into a thicket there; instead of having fun he thought he would be killed before he finally rolled to the bottom of the canyon. Since his hands and feet were tied, he could barely get up; but when he finally did get up and looked around, the rabbit had already run off and was nowhere to be seen.

The bear, groaning with pain, crossed over the mountain, and there was the rabbit making *miso* [salty bean paste]. "Rabbit-*dono,* rabbit-*dono,* you played a mean trick on me which nearly killed me; just look at the wounds I got from it. What did you do it for anyway?" said the bear.

The rabbit looked more innocent than he had the time before. "That was the rabbit from Wisteria Mountain, the rabbit from Wisteria Mountain. I am the rabbit from *Miso* Mountain, the rabbit from *Miso* Mountain. I know nothing about it."

The bear believed what he was told, thinking that the rabbit was surely right. "By the way, rabbit-*dono* from *Miso* Mountain, what is this stuff that you are making now?"

"Oh, this is what I call *miso.* It is a special medicine for burns, bruises, or scratches. If you smear some on your wounds, they will heal immediately. I was making this to take to the village to sell."

The bear wanted to have some so badly that he could hardly stand it. "Rabbit-*dono,* rabbit-*dono,* here I have such painful burns and bruises; please let me have just a little of it."

"Well then, I'll give you a little," and going around to the bear's back, he took some of the *miso* and smeared it into the bear's open wounds. Gradually the saltiness of the *miso* penetrated the wounds, and they began to sting so that it was unbearable; but the rabbit had already run away and disappeared.

The bear, crying with agony, went down to the river's edge to wash off the *miso*. He finally got it all off, and groaning with pain, he crossed over the mountain. There he found the rabbit again; he was busily cutting down trees and sawing them into boards. The bear struggled up to where the rabbit was. "Rabbit-*dono*, rabbit-*dono*, you have really treated me cruelly. Because of you my body is swollen like this. Why did you do it to me?" he asked rebukingly.

"That was the rabbit from *Miso* Mountain, the rabbit from *Miso* Mountain. I am Cedar Mountain rabbit, Cedar Mountain rabbit. I know nothing about it," he said, pretending innocence.

The bear thought that what the rabbit said was reasonable enough. "By the way," he asked, "what are you planning to do with the cedar boards you are sawing?"

"I am going to make a boat with them, then row out on the river and catch all the fish I want," said the Cedar Mountain rabbit.

"That sounds interesting," said the bear. "Rabbit-*dono*, rabbit-*dono*, please take me as your companion," and so the two of them began to work on the boat. They discussed the matter and decided that since the rabbit was white they should build a boat from the white cedar boards for him. Since the bear was black, they decided to build a black earthen boat for him. So the bear built a black earthen boat and the rabbit a white cedar one; then they took them down to the river, climbed in, and set them afloat.

Since the bear's boat was made of mud it was likely to fall apart anyway, but the rabbit, safe in his boat of cedar, purposely rammed the bear's boat, and it slowly began to sink.

"Rabbit-*dono*, rabbit-*dono*, help me, please!" shouted the bear.

"All right, I'm coming," said the rabbit, but in the meantime the earthen boat fell apart and the bear fell with a splash into the water. The rabbit, pretending to rescue the bear, took an oar and called out, "Bear-*dono*, climb on to this, bear-*dono*, climb on to this." He pushed the bear to the bottom of a deep pool and so finally killed him.

The rabbit dragged the bear out of the pool and over to a nearby house. There he borrowed a kettle, having decided to boil the bear and make soup. All the grownups had gone to the fields, and only the children were left to watch the house; so the rabbit and the children made the bear into soup and ate it all, leaving only the bones and the head.

"Now, you children, when your father and mother come home, you must tell them to bang on this key and dance around and around, chewing as hard as they can on the bones of the bear's head. I shall go to the mountain behind the house and sleep there, but you must not tell where I am," and so the rabbit left.

Soon the children's parents returned from the fields, and the children told them what the rabbit had told them to do. The parents took the key and banged on it as they danced around in circles, chewing on the bones of the bear's head. They continued to bang the key, dance in circles, and chew the bones until they had broken all their teeth.

"That beast of a rabbit, he has tricked us into breaking all our teeth," cried the parents, becoming very, very angry. "Children, where is that rabbit?" they demanded.

Although the rabbit had told the children not to tell where he was, the parents forced them to tell. Finally they revealed that he had gone to the mountain behind the house and was sleeping.

The parents grabbed the kettle hook and rushed out to where the children had told them; there they found the rabbit asleep. They knocked him about with the kettle hook, crying: "You awful rabbit, because of you we have lost all our teeth. What a hateful beast you are! We are going to kill you! Children, run and get the sword we keep beside our pillow."

The children ran home, but thinking that they had been told to bring the pillow, they got a pillow and returned with it to their parents.

"You foolish brats, we didn't say the pillow; we said to bring the sword from beside the pillow. If you can't understand that, go and bring the kitchen knife off the chopping board."

The children understood that they were to bring the chopping board; so they ran and got it.

"What foolish brats you are! Well then, take the chopping board and hold the rabbit down so that he can't escape," and they ran off themselves to get the kitchen knife.

The rabbit soon thought of a plan of escape. "Children," he asked, "about how big do you suppose your mother's head is?"

The children took one hand and described about how big it was. "I can't tell from that," said the rabbit, "show me with both hands."

"It's about this big," they said, letting go of the board with both hands. The rabbit, seeing the chance he had waited for, escaped.

Just then the parents returned. Seeing the rabbit running away, they threw the knife at him. It hit his tail and cut it off, and since that time the rabbit has had no tail.

Dotto harai. "With this, it's sold out."

·4· *The Quail and the Badger*

Motif K561, "Escape by persuading captor to talk," found here, is common to a number of animal tales in European tradition, e.g. Types 6, 57, 111, 122, 227. Some of these types are popular in India as well. This tale is Kata No. 36, "The Quail and the Badger." Collected in Saso-gun, Kumamoto-ken.

Eleven versions of this tale have been recorded in Japan. Ikeda, p. 37, reports that it is found in Mongolia in much the same form as in Japan. Chaucer used this motif to good effect in the Nun's Priest's tale where the cock tricks the fox into talking and thus escapes.

In feudal Japan, when the procession of a nobleman or high government official passed by, all the peasants were required to kneel in obeisance. In an animal story, this requirement would naturally extend to beasts, so that the quail could expect to be struck at for ignoring the procession.

· THE QUAIL and the badger once happened to meet on the road. "Today I'd like to show you a nobleman's procession; how about changing yourself into a roadside stake?" proposed the quail.

The badger agreed and transformed himself into a roadside stake. He stood stiffly by the side of the road, while the quail haughtily sat on his head. Soon a tall palanquin bearer came by, carrying a six-*shaku* [about six feet] -long pole over his shoulder. The palanquin bearer passed by the strange-looking figure of the badger and quail, but the quail paid no attention and made no move to fly away.

"What an impudent bird you are," cried the bearer, and raising his pole, he struck at the quail who was still sitting on the head of the disguised badger. Just at that moment the quail hopped lightly away. When the bearer saw this he laughed, but the badger became very angry.

"You told me that you were going to show me a nobleman's procession and had me transform myself into a roadside stake. Because of that I get beaten, but you just fly off and pay no attention." Saying this the badger pounced on the quail and caught him in his mouth.

The quail, caught fast in the badger's mouth, could not move. "Ah, my poor mother, if you eat me up like this, I cannot give her a last farewell. Please, will you call her for me."

"All right," said the badger, "I'll call once," and raising his voice, he called the quail's mother. As soon as the badger opened his mouth to call, the quail flew out and escaped. The badger became angry again and grabbed the quail's tail. The quail knew that if he did not escape this time, he would lose his life, and so he pulled with all his might and finally pulled his tail off. And that is why to this day the quail has no tail.

• 5 • The Monkey and the Crab

The cycle in which this and the following tale are found has been assigned by Ikeda, pp. 29–36, to Type 9, The Unjust Partner. Kata No. 52B, "Monkey Cheats Crab." Collected in Isshaya City, Kitataki-gun, Nagasaki-ken, by Kenso Orito.

This tale is part of the Saru-Kani Kassen *("Monkey-Crab Battle") cycle widely told throughout Japan. One hundred and forty-two versions of the cycle have been reported. The concluding part of the text given here, containing Motif A2376, "Animal*

characteristics, claws," is often replaced by Type 210, Cock, Hen,
Duck, Pin, and Needle on a Journey, *in which various strategi-
cally placed objects punish the evil monkey. Ikeda, pp. 32–33,
however, considers the "why-so" sequel to belong to the original
form of the tale.*

• LONG, LONG ago there lived a monkey and a crab. The monkey
had picked up a persimmon seed, and the crab had a pressed rice
ball. The monkey said, "Crab-*don*, crab-*don*, how about trading
my persimmon seed for your rice ball," and so they traded. The
crab took the persimmon seed and planted it in his front field.
Day by day it grew bigger and bigger, and after a while there
were splendid persimmons on it. The crab went to the monkey's
place and asked him to come pick the persimmons for him.

The monkey readily agreed and climbed up in the tree. He
ate the ripe fruit himself and threw the green ones down at the
crab. The crab became angry and ran away, all the while calling
the monkey bad names. The monkey became angry and chased
the crab into its hole, then he started to defecate into the crab's
burrow. The crab took his scissor claws and fastened them
securely onto the monkey's buttocks. This hurt so much that
the monkey cried: "Crab-*don*, crab-*don*, please let me loose. If
you will, I'll give you three hairs from my buttocks." And so
that is why there are hairs growing on the crab's scissor claws.

•6• *The Monkey and the Pheasant*

*The first part of this tale employs Motif K495, "Trickster shams
sickness so that partner does all the work." The latter part cor-
responds to Type 210,* Cock, Hen, Duck, Pin, and Needle on a
Journey. *Kata No. 53, "The Battle of the Monkey and the Crab."
Collected in Yazawa-mura, Hienuki-gun, Iwate-ken, from Takeo
Furukawa.*

This tale is part of the widely distributed Saru-Kani Kassen
*("Monkey-Crab Battle") cycle, elements of which combine freely
to form separate tales.*

Antti Aarne, the distinguished Finnish folklorist, made a study of Type 210, the tale in which various objects hide in strategic places and co-operate to kill or harm an opponent. He concluded that the tale originated in Asia and spread to Europe. The motif is clearly well known in Japan; some sixty versions of the "Monkey-Crab Battle" cycle containing the motif have been recorded. Eberhard, pp. 25–27, lists twenty-six variants from China; Thompson and Roberts, p. 39, give reference to eleven versions in India.

The fact that the monkey failed to use a suffix of familiarity or respect when he called the pheasant as he came to take revenge indicates his feeling of hatred and anger. It is usually only at such times that the polite name-suffixes are omitted.

• THE MONKEY and the pheasant had a rice paddy together. The time came to repair the paths around the field, and the pheasant said, "Monkey-*morai*, monkey-*morai*, everyone else is repairing their rice paddy terraces; we should do ours too."

"Well, you know, pheasant-*morai*, my feet hurt me so badly, I can't go out and repair terraces."

"Well, that's all right then, you stay home and take care of yourself. I will go and repair them," and so the pheasant set off alone and repaired the terraces.

The days passed and the time came to spade up the field. The pheasant said, "Monkey-*morai*, monkey-*morai*, everyone else is beginning to spade up their fields; we should do ours too."

"Today my head aches so that I'm not able to do a thing."

"All right," said the pheasant, and he went and spaded the field by himself.

After a while the pheasant said, "Monkey-*morai*, monkey-*morai*, everywhere else they are beginning to set out the rice plants; we should set ours out too."

"Now what shall I do! For the past two or three days I have had a terrible cough and I just can't do a thing."

"All right," said the pheasant, and there was nothing he could do but go and set out the rice plants himself.

The paddies were watered, the grass around them was cut, the summer dog days passed, and it became autumn. The countless heads of rice hung in orderly rows, and the time for harvest neared. "Monkey-*morai*, monkey-*morai*, everyone else has begun harvesting their rice; we should gather ours too."

"For some reason my back hurts, my hands and feet pain me so, and my head aches so that I can hardly stand it."

"All right, all right," said the pheasant, not saying a word in complaint. The pheasant worked very hard and harvested the rice all by himself. He threshed it, and finally the rice was finished.

The monkey then said to the pheasant, "Well, well, pheasant-*morai*, pheasant-*morai*, you have worked very hard up until now; today let's make some *mochi* [pounded rice dough] and eat it."

"All right, all right," said the pheasant in agreement, and so the pheasant and the monkey began to make *mochi*. They steamed the rice in the rice steamer, then took out the *mochi* mortar and pestle and began pounding the rice, *bettara bettara,* thump-whack, thump-whack.

When they finished the *mochi*, the monkey said, "Pheasant-*morai*, pheasant-*morai*, please go and get some rinse water."

"All right, all right," said the pheasant, and he went to get a bucket to fetch water from the kitchen. While he was gone, the monkey took the *mochi* out of the mortar, stuck it on the end of the pestle and ran galloping, *essara essara,* for the mountains.

"Oh, oh, what a wretched fellow that monkey is!" cried the pheasant and set off after him, but he could find him nowhere. The greedy monkey ran along without watching carefully and the *mochi* fell off as he was going through a thicket, but he did not notice it.

"The pheasant must be weeping now," said the monkey to himself, and he continued on until he got to the top of the mountain. He took the pestle from his shoulder, but the *mochi* was gone. "Now, where has the *mochi* gone?" cried the monkey. He turned around and retraced his steps, carefully looking for the *mochi*. After a while he came upon the pheasant in the thicket, he was picking the dirt off the *mochi* and *shinmeri shinmeri*, peck, peck, peck, was eating the *mochi*.

"Oh, pheasant-*morai*, pheasant-*morai*, is this where you are? What does that thicket *mochi* taste like?"

"Well, is it monkey-*morai*? If you pick the dirt off the thicket *mochi* as you eat it, it is delicious."

"Then please give me just a little."

"Monkey-*morai*, you can have the *mochi* that is stuck on the pestle; I am blowing the dirt off the thicket *mochi* and eating it."

"I don't care what you're doing, please give me a little."

"I won't give you even a little bit."

"All right then, this evening I will come and take revenge on you, remember that!" The monkey became very angry and ran off into the mountains.

When the pheasant saw that he had made the monkey angry, he became a little worried. He returned home and began sobbing, *oi oi*, when just then an egg came rolling, *koro koro*, over and over, up to him. "What are you crying for, pheasant-*morai*?" asked the egg.

"The monkey has said that he will come and take revenge on me tonight, and I am so scared that I'm crying like this."

"What! That is nothing to cry about. I will help you out," said the egg, but still the pheasant kept on crying, *oi oi*. Soon a door bar came plodding by, *bikutari bikutari*, clomp, clomp, and said, "Pheasant-*morai*, pheasant-*morai*, what are you crying about?"

"It's nothing except that the monkey is coming tonight to take revenge on me, and so I am crying."

"I'll help you, too, so don't cry any more," said the door bar, but even at that the pheasant kept crying, *oi oi*. Soon an earwig came; then a bitter bug came; then a *tatami* needle came. Also a horse-feed mortar came and some dung came. They all said, "Pheasant-*morai*, pheasant-*morai*, there's nothing to cry about. We will all help you," and so finally the pheasant stopped worrying and crying.

Evening drew near. The door bar went to the entrance way, the egg went to the fireplace, the *tatami* needle went to the side of the fireplace, the earwig got in the water kettle, the bitter bug got in the *miso* [salty bean paste] tub, the dung spread itself on the step leading into the garden, and the horse-feed mortar climbed up into the rafters above the ceiling. Each one went to his own place and waited for the monkey to come.

Night fell. In the distance the monkey could be heard: "Pheasant, pheasant, I've come to get revenge. Pheasant, pheasant, are you there?" Soon the monkey got to the pheasant's house, but it was dark and silent. "Pheasant, pheasant, open the door! It's the monkey, I've come for my revenge," called the monkey, shouting as loud as he could.

The house remained silent. "Are you going to open the door or aren't you. If you don't open it, I'll come in anyway," and he slammed the door open with a bang. When he did that, the door bar hit him on the head.

"Who was that? What hit me on the head? Brr, it's cold here." The monkey went over to the fireplace and began to blow on the fire. Just then the egg burst open. "Ouch, it's hot, it's hot!" cried the monkey and holding his hands over his genitals, he fell over backward on his rear end. When he did that, the *tatami* needle stuck right up his anus. "It's hot, it hurts, *miso* is a good salve for burns," he cried and ran over to the tub of *miso*. He intended to smear some on his burns but by mistake got it in his mouth and bit down on the bitter bug. "Oh, it's bitter, it's bitter," he cried and running over to the kettle of water, plunged his head in. When he did that the earwig reached out and bit off his tongue.

"Instead of my getting revenge on the pheasant, he has been revenged on me!" cried the monkey in surprise, and tried his best to escape, but as he did so, he slipped on the dung and fell head over heels.

"Now is the time to finish off that greedy monkey," cried the horse-feed mortar, and tumbling out of the rafters, he completed the revenge on the monkey.

Dondo harai. "With this, it's sold out."

·7· The Wolf's Reward

Type 156, Thorn Removed from Lion's Paw (Androcles and the Lion). *Kata No. 119, "The Grateful Wolf." Collected in*

Iida-mura, Shimoina-gun, Nagano-ken, from the mother of the collector, Kiyomi Iwasaki.

This tale is quite common in Japan and is often told as having actually happened. The grateful animal is most often a wolf, sometimes a bear, but not a lion as in the story of Androcles. Dorson (Folk Legends of Japan, pp. 143–44) gives the legend of a blacksmith who helped a wolf in the throes of childbirth. Later he married a beautiful woman who proved to be the wolf transformed and who bore him hairy-chested children.

• Long ago in a certain place there lived a young man. One night he suddenly had to go to the village on the other side of the mountain pass on business. The night was very dark, and in the mountain pass there were places where the trees grew so thick that it was frightening, even in daytime. The young man was climbing up through the pass, along just such a place, when from somewhere up ahead he heard a strange sound.

"That must be that badger playing tricks again," he thought to himself and continued on his way, but the sound was different from that the badger made; it was a sort of rumbling growl, like snoring. Wondering what it could be, he took his paper lantern and went over to see what it was. There he found a huge wolf, his mouth open, stretching his neck in and out but not trying to run away at all. Thinking this quite strange, the young man went up close to where the wolf was.

The wolf, who up until then had been standing, kneeled down on his front legs as if to bow. It looked as if he were begging for help.

The young man looked closely and saw that something was stuck in the wolf's throat. "Here, I'll take it out for you," he said, and slipping one arm out of his kimono, he put his hand down the wolf's throat and pulled out a big thick bone. "After this you must be more careful when you eat big bones like that," said the young man.

The wolf, yipping softly, *kun kun,* in relief, slipped off into the mountains, rustling the grass, *kasa kasa.*

Several days passed. The young man was invited to a harvest celebration in the neighborhood. They were in the middle of the feast when a wolf was heard to growl at the front door. Everyone turned pale and began shaking with fright. The young man said, "I will go and see what it is." He went to the front door and saw that it was the wolf whom he had helped on the mountain pass. When the wolf saw the young man's face, he suddenly became as quiet as a kitten. He came up to the man's feet, and when the young man petted his head, he licked his hand in joy.

"Are you so happy about what I did for you that time?" said the young man. And then the wolf took something black that he had beside him and dropped it with a thud by the door; then *goso goso,* he slipped silently away.

The young man looked closely and saw that the wolf had brought him a huge pheasant. It was his way of thanking the young man for the favor he had received.

•8• *The Greedy Hawk*

The episode of the wren and the boar contains Motif L315.1, "Bird flies into large animal's ear and kills him," and is found in Type 228, The Titmouse Tries To Be as Big as a Bear. Kata No. 49, "The Wren as King of the Birds," and No. 50, "The Hawk and the Wren." Collected in Mizusawa-mura, Isawa-gun, Iwate-ken, from the servant of collector Tari Moriguchi.

Twenty-three versions of this tale have been reported in Japan. In some the small bird is elected king after various exploits, in others he is merely praised. The latter episode of the present text is often told as a separate tale. A variant appears in the eighth-century Nihongi, *the oldest recorded history of Japan, where it is told, p. 298, as having occurred during the reign of Emperor Nintoku in* A.D. *379. Chaucer used the theme of strife among the birds in his* Parlement of Foules.

• ONE DAY the eagle, who was the leader and also the largest of all the birds, got caught in the fork of a tree. No matter how much he struggled, he could not get loose. A great number of birds came and tried to help him. They pulled on his feathers until finally his feathers were all pulled out and his body was bare and red.

After a while a riverbear bird came by. "You shouldn't go about it like that," he said. He had all the birds get on the branches to the right and left of the fork of the tree. With the weight of the birds on the branches, the fork of the tree split open and the eagle could go free.

Since the eagle's life had been saved, he decided to give a feast in celebration. The riverbear bird, saying that he would bring all the food to eat, flew off to the mountains. Soon a wild boar came toward him. The riverbear bird flew into the wild boar's ear and buzzed around. The wild boar was in such great pain that it died, and the riverbear bird very proudly took it back to where all the other birds were gathered.

The hawk saw this and said, "Well, I will go and show you that I can get two wild boars," and he flew off to the river. He went along and saw two wild boars together, coming toward him. "Those are just right; I'll take both of them at once," and he sank the talons of both feet, left and right, into the wild boars' backs, catching both boars at the same time.

The boars were very surprised and dashed off in opposite directions. If he had tried to get just one boar it would have been all right, but since he had tried to get both of them at once, the hawk's legs were broken and his talons were pulled out.

It is said that this is the origin of the proverb, "The greedy hawk gets his talons pulled out."

•9• *The Whale and the Sea Slug*

Type 275, The Race of the Fox and the Crayfish. Kata No. 45, "The Race of the Tiger and the Fox." Collected in Oshima-gun, Yamaguchi-ken.

This tale is related to the classic race of the hare and the tor-

toise found in Aesop; Thompson, p. 196, reports that it is even more popular in oral tradition in most of the world than is the Aesopian fable. He notes that it is found in Europe and is well known in eastern Asia, all parts of Africa, and among Indians in both North and South America. The Japanese tradition, according to Ikeda, p. 69, is represented by four distinct versions.

• LONG AGO the whale was bragging, "There is no greater animal than I," and the sea slug heard him and laughed. The whale became angry and said, "All right then, let's run a race," and the sea slug agreed. "Let's wait three days; we will decide the time and place, and then we will meet one another at the beach at Yura," and so the agreement was made.

The sea slug then went and gathered up all his friends. "To tell the truth," he said, "I agreed today to run a race with the whale, but of course I can't win; so I want you to go, one to each of the beaches around here, and when the whale comes by, you must call out, 'Are you just now getting here?'" All agreed and so they went tumbling off, one to each of the beaches in the vicinity.

Three days passed and the whale and the sea slug met at the beach at Yura. "Let's swim to the beach at Kohama," they said and set off. The whale swam swiftly and powerfully, but the sea slug could only roll and tumble along with great difficulty. The whale reached the beach at Kohama and thinking that the sea slug surely couldn't be there yet, called out just to make sure, "Sea slug-*dono*, sea slug-*dono*." He was surprised to hear, "Whale-*dono*, are you just now getting here?" The sea slug suggested that they swim next to the beach at Shimoda.

The whale swam off, and when he got to the beach at Shimoda, he looked around and called out, "Sea slug-*dono*, sea slug-*dono*." The sea slug answered, "Are you just now coming, whale-*dono*?"

Next they swam to the beach at Mori; but no matter where the whale swam to, the sea slug was always there first, and so finally the whale realized that he was defeated.

· 10 · The Cat and the Crab

Type 275, The Race of the Fox and the Crayfish. Kata No. 41,
"The Mudsnail and the Fox." Collected in Kikai Island, Oshima-
gun, Kagoshima-ken, from Saneyoshi Tomi.

This tale appears in Aesop. Thompson, p. 197, reports that it
is known all over Europe and is a favorite in Africa and in the
Negro and Indian traditions of America. The only Asian tradition
he cites is that of Indonesia, but Ikeda, p. 70, states that twenty-
three versions have been recorded in Japan. They often take the
form of an international match involving a Japanese fox and a
Chinese lion or Korean tiger. The Japanese fox always wins.
Aesop's fable of the hare and the tortoise is commonly known in
Japan through school texts, but only two versions of a folk nature
have been reported.

• ONCE THE CAT and the crab decided to have a race. The cat
thought to himself, "No matter how fast the crab runs sideways,
he will be no match for me," and so he decided to take it easy.
However just as they began the race, the sly crab attached himself to the cat's tail. The cat never noticed and set off as fast as
he could run and soon came to the goal. Wondering how the
crab was doing, he turned around and just at that moment, the
crab let loose his tail and called out, "Cat-*dono*, cat-*dono*, are you
just now arriving?"

The cat turned around in surprise, and sure enough, there was
the crab with one foot over the goal line. The cat was beaten and
hanging his head, admitted his defeat.

· 11 · The Monkey's Liver

Type 91, Monkey (Cat) Who Left His Heart at Home. Kata
No. 61, "The Monkey's Liver." Collected on Kikai Island,
Oshima-gun, Kagoshima-ken, from Saneyoshi Tomi.

This tale is very popular in Japan. The desire for monkey's liver is often said to be a craving of pregnancy. The tale appears in the well-known eleventh-century compilation, Konjaku Monogatori, *translated by S. W. Jones, pp. 26–27, in the section on tales derived from India. It is included, as well, in the Pali* Jātaka, *edited by E. B. Cowell, Vol. II, 110–12, a collection of Buddha birth stories. It is known in Europe but is found much more frequently in Asia. Thompson and Roberts, p. 28, list nine variants of the tale found in India.*

• LONG AGO, the only daughter of the deity of Neinya [dragon kingdom of the sea] became ill and a priest was called to give a divination. The priest divined its cause and said, "This disease will never be cured unless you get the fresh raw liver of a monkey and feed it to the girl." So the deity of the dragon kingdom sent a dog to a far country to find a monkey.

The dog went to a distant island and finally found a monkey. "Monkey-*dono,* monkey-*dono,* have you ever thought about going sightseeing to a place called Neinya?"

"Yes, I have thought that I would like to go there at least once."

"Then I will take you with me. Just hang on to my hips and we will be in Neinya before you can blink your eyes."

The monkey happily hung onto the dog's waist and they went to the seashore. It seemed as if the dog had only taken one step from a steppingstone and instantly the two of them were in Neinya.

After they got to Neinya the monkey was entertained for a while, but one day the octopus and the spined swellfish said to him: "You're in a terrible fix here, you know. Actually the deity of Neinya intends to give your liver to his only daughter, and so you don't have much longer to live."

Having been told this secret, the monkey became very worried and decided to escape in some way or other. "I did a stupid thing, I came here and left my liver at home," he said.

The deity of Neinya heard about what the monkey had said and declared, "Well, if you forgot your liver, there is nothing to do but to hurry and go to get it." So he sent him off with the dog again. When they got to the island, the monkey ran away as fast as he could and never allowed himself to be caught again.

Afterward it was discovered that it was the octopus and the spiny swellfish who had betrayed the secret. By way of punishment, the octopus had all his bones pulled out and the spiny swellfish was beaten until his bones stuck out all over him, and that is why he is covered with spines even to this day.

•12• The Rain Leak in an Old House

Motif N691.1, "Numskull's outcry overawes tiger who is carrying him on his back," is applicable here. Kata No. 74, "The Rain Leak in an Old House." Collected in Yunomae-mura, Kumagun, Kumamoto-ken, from Taichi Kohama.

There are seventy-seven examples of this tale recorded in Japan. Eberhard, pp. 18–19, lists six variants from China, while Thompson and Balys, p. 371, note one tale from India containing the above motif. Ikeda, pp. 251–52, reports it from Korea. There is no record of the tale being known in Europe.

Rain leaking through the rotting thatch of an abandoned house typifies an eerie, ghostly scene.

• ONCE LONG AGO in a certain place in the middle of the mountains there lived an old man and an old woman. The old man and his wife liked horses very much and had a splendid one of their own. One time a thief decided to steal their horse and sneaked into their house at night. He climbed up into the rafters of the stable and waited, but no matter how long he waited, the horse did not return to the barn. The thief became sleepy and fell fast asleep.

The tiger-wolf who lived in that part of the mountains decided to catch the old man and the old woman and eat them, and so he went to their house. The tiger-wolf always thought to himself, "I am the strongest thing in the whole world." The old man and his wife were talking to one another, and the tiger-wolf listened. The old man said, "Old woman, old woman, what do you think is the most frightening thing in the world?"

The old woman replied, "I think the most frightening thing in the world is the tiger-wolf.

When the tiger-wolf heard that, he was triumphant. He felt certain that he could catch both the old people and eat them that very night. Then the old woman asked the old man, "What do you think is the most frightening thing in the world?" The old man replied, "I think that a rain leak in an old house is the most frightening thing in the world."

When he heard this the tiger-wolf was very surprised. "Here I thought that I was the strongest one in the whole world but this fellow called Rain-Leak-in-an-Old-House must be even stronger," and he began to shake with fright. Just then the thief woke up. He looked down and saw what looked like a horse below him. "That must be the horse which the old man keeps," he thought and jumped down on to it.

When he did this the tiger-wolf was so surprised that he sprang out of the stable thinking, "This must be that Rain-Leak-in-an-Old-House fellow that they were talking about," and he ran with all his might to one of his companions and crawled into his den. The thief, thinking that it was the horse, did not want to let go, and held on very tightly. He got off at the mouth of the den and waited outside until the animal came out again.

As soon as the tiger-wolf was in the den he told the leader of the animals about Rain-Leak-in-an-Old-House.

"Who will go and capture that fellow Rain-Leak-in-an-Old-House?" asked the leader of the animals.

Everyone was afraid and all said, "I won't go," "I don't want to go," but the monkey, who was very clever, volunteered to go.

The monkey stuck his tail outside the den. The thief, waiting outside, saw it and thought it was the horse's tail. He grabbed hold of it and pulled with all his might. The monkey thought that he had been taken hold of by Rain-Leak-in-an-Old-House and began pulling with all his might from inside the den. The thief pulled from above and the monkey pulled from below, and finally the monkey's tail snapped in two.

Although the monkey used to have lots of hair on his face and his tail was very long, at that time his face bumped against the rocks and rubbed the hair off, leaving his face red. It is also since then that his tail has been very short.

Shimyaa. "It's finished."

·13· *The Mole's Bridegroom*

Type 2031C, The Man Seeks the Greatest Being as a Husband for His Daughter. Kata No. 70, "The Mole's Bridegroom." Collected in Kuzumaki-mura, Minami Kanbara-gun, Niigata-ken, from Etsu Makino.

Thompson, p. 232, states that this tale is essentially literary, being found in Oriental tale collections and appearing frequently in medieval literature. Ikeda, p. 318, notes that it is recorded in the thirteenth-century Japanese collection, Saseki Shu, *a source book of Buddhist sermons compiled by the monk Muju. The tale enjoys wide popularity in present-day Japan, where it often appears in children's books and has been recorded in oral tradition. Thompson and Roberts, p. 169, give references to eight Indian variants.*

The mouse or rat, rather than the mole as in the text given here, is often the central figure in the tale in Japan, as it is in most versions from other countries.

· THE MOLE had a very beautiful daughter. "I want to marry my daughter to the greatest person in all Japan," he said, calling all the moles together to discuss it with them.

"The sun is the greatest thing in all Japan," said one of them.

"Then I shall marry her to the sun."

"But the sky is higher than the sun; the sky is the greatest of all."

"Then I shall marry her to the sky."

"But the sky is sometimes covered by clouds; the clouds are the greatest thing of all."

"Then I shall marry her to the clouds."

"No, no matter how many clouds there are, the wind can blow them away; the wind is greatest of all."

"Then I shall marry her to the wind."

"No, no. When the wind blows, no matter how much it blows and no matter how much rain falls, the river banks do not move; the greatest thing in all Japan is the river banks."

"Then I shall marry her to the river banks."

"But no matter how strong the river banks are, moles can make holes in them, so the greatest thing in all Japan, no matter what one says, is a mole."

"Then I shall marry her to a mole."

And so that is why the mole's daughter was married to a mole.

14 *An Endless Story*

Type 2300, Endless Tales. Kata No. 457, "Endless Tales." Collected in Kami Mashiki-gun, Kumamota-ken, from Kakuko Cho.

Thompson, p. 230, notes that so-called endless tales are well known all over Europe and are especially popular in Hungary. The tale given here is but one of a number of examples of this type found in Japan.

• LONG AGO all the rats in Nagasaki got together and decided that since there was nothing left to eat in Nagasaki, they would cross over to Satsuma. They boarded a ship and set out. It happened that on the way they met a ship on which all the rats in Satsuma had gone aboard, intending to go to Nagasaki. They asked one another how things were and discovered that there was nothing to eat in either Satsuma or Nagasaki. There was no use in going to Nagasaki nor any use in going to Satsuma, so they decided to jump into the sea and drown.

The first rat began to cry, *chu chu,* and jumped over with a splash. Then another rat cried, *chu chu,* and jumped over with a splash. Then another cried, *chu chu,* and jumped over with a splash . . . .

Part II
Ogres

Type 300, The Dragon Slayer. Kata No. 91A, "Conquering the Monkey Demon." Collected in Mono-gun, Miyagi-ken, by Keisuke Sugawara.

The eminent German folklorist, Kurt Ranke, has made a detailed study of Type 300 and the related Type 303, The Twins or Blood Brothers. Thompson, pp. 31–32, reports Ranke's conclusion that the episodes of the dragon-slaying, the rescue of the maiden, and her marriage to the hero were first combined in France. Ranke had only one Japanese variant available and felt that the appearance of the tale in Japan was merely sporadic. In fact, however, a tale very similar to The Dragon Slayer *is old in Japan. The eighth-century* Kojiki, *one of the two oldest recorded Japanese histories, pp. 71–73, includes, among a large number of myths and legends, a version of the dragon-slaying tale in which Susanowo, brother of the Sun Goddess, is the hero. Elements of the Susanowo myth have persisted in oral tradition in the tale of Shippei Taro. This tale is distributed throughout Japan, twenty-six versions having been recorded.*

Thompson and Roberts, pp. 44–45, report some thirty-five versions of this tale type from India; the Chinese use of the dragon motif in various forms is, of course, well known. The age and strength of the tradition in the Orient would seem to warrant additional study of this tale.

• LONG AGO there was an itinerant priest. One day as he was wandering from place to place, he came to a lonely mountain village. For some reason, at every house in the village, *mochi* was being made. The priest thought that perhaps there would soon be some sort of festival. He walked about looking around; then he saw that in one house in the whole village, there was no *mochi* being made. It was a beautiful large mansion, but it was so silent that it appeared that no one was there at all.

The priest thought this very strange. He listened carefully and could hear that everyone in the house was crying.

"What a strange thing this is," thought the priest and entered the house. When he was inside he could see that everyone was gathered together around a young girl, and they were all weeping over her.

"Excuse me, please, but why are you crying?" asked the priest. The man who appeared to be the master of the house finally stopped crying and said: "After seven days, we must make a human sacrifice. On the mountain over there, there is an old shrine dedicated to some deity; no one any longer knows what god it is, but every year at harvest time, a young girl must be offered to it. If we do not make the offering, a great storm will come, and our rice paddies and fields will be ravaged; so we can do nothing but make the offering. This year it is our turn, and since we must offer up our only daughter, we are mourning for her."

The priest listened in silence. Then he said, "Is there really anything like that in this world? Instead of your daughter, I will become the offering, and she will not need to go."

The priest climbed the mountain to where the shrine was. There on the mountain he saw an old ruined temple. There was a hole in a huge pine tree which stood by the temple, and the priest hid himself in it. When midnight came a great horde of some sort of beings came swarming up to the temple and gathered in front of it. One who appeared to be the leader asked in a loud voice, "Is Shippei Taro here?" One of the creatures replied, "Shippei Taro won't come tonight." Then the doors of the temple were opened, and all the creatures went inside. The priest listened from his hole and heard this song,

> Don't tell that and don't tell this,
> Don't tell it to Shippei Taro,
> At Nagahama in the province of Oumi,
> Don't tell it to Shippei Taro.
> *Suten, sutten, sutten ten.* Bim bam, bim bam.

They sang this song over and over, and as the priest listened he thought to himself that no matter what sort of *bakemono* [ogre; bogey] they were, they could surely be conquered by someone named Shippei Taro.

That night he returned to the girl's house in the village; then he set out for the town of Nagahama in the province of Oumi to hunt for Shippei Taro. When he came to the province of Oumi, he began asking at every house if they knew where a man named Shippei Taro lived; but no matter where he asked, no one knew anyone by that name. Filled with disappointment, the priest was sitting idly on a stone by the roadside when a huge spotted dog, as big as a calf, came by. "That is a big dog; a dog like that could surely conquer the *bakemono*," he thought to himself, when just then the dog's master came along calling, "Shippei Taro."

The priest suddenly regained his spirits. He told the master that he would like to borrow his dog in order to rescue the girl, and the dog's master gladly loaned him the animal. The priest, accompanied by the dog, set off for the girl's village as fast as he could go.

The seventh day, the day of the sacrifice, came, but the priest had not returned to the village. There was nothing the girl's family could do but prepare to sacrifice her. A long wooden chest was brought and the girl was dressed in a white kimono [death shroud]. The whole family sobbed as if their hearts would break. Some of the villagers felt sorry for her, and they too began crying, while others said cruelly: "What are you doing, waiting and waiting? Hurry up and offer the girl; if you don't, there will be a terrible storm like there was before."

"Wait just a little while," said the girl's parents and continued to wait for the priest's return. But as the priest did not return, they finally had to put the girl in the wooden chest. Just as the villagers were about to pick up the chest to carry it up the mountain, the priest, accompanied by Shippei Taro, came running up, puffing and panting. They took the sobbing, frightened girl from the wooden chest and put both the priest and the dog in it instead. "Now take us and offer us to the deity instead of the girl," requested the priest.

"If we did that, the deity would punish us," said some of the villagers, but others took the wooden chest with the priest and dog in it and carried it up the mountain. They put it down in front of the shrine; then without looking behind them, they ran back down the mountain.

When midnight came a large number of the *bakemono* gathered by the temple. They sang as they danced around and around the wooden chest,

> Don't tell that and don't tell this,
> Don't tell it to Shippei Taro,
> At Nagahama in the province of Oumi,
> Don't tell it to Shippei Taro.
> *Suten, sutten, sutten ten*. Bim bam, bim bam.

Soon they began to take the lid off the wooden chest. Just then Shippei Taro let out a howl and jumped from the box. He began to attack the *bakemono*. The priest also jumped out and began to cut them down.

The next morning the villagers said to themselves, "By now that priest has surely been eaten by the deity," and they climbed the mountain to see. There they saw dead monkeys lying about everywhere. A huge baboon with hair as stiff as needles lay dead, his throat torn open by Shippei Taro.

After that it was no longer necessary to make human sacrifices, and everyone could live in peace.

Konde oshimai. "This is the end."

· *16* ·   *The* Oni's *Laughter*

Motifs R111.1.1, "Rescue of princess from ogre," and D1110, "Magic conveyances," are the principal motifs appearing in this tale. The final escape from the ogres is a novel twist of Motif D670, "Magic flight." Kata No. 82A. "Kozuna, the Oni's Child." Collected in Kuzumaki-mura, Minami Kanbara-gun, Niigata-ken, from Etsu Makino.

Thirty versions of this tale have been collected in Japan. Ikeda, p. 78, reports that a number of Chinese versions have been recorded, but Eberhard does not include the tale in his type index of Chinese tales. The tale, as it is found in Japan, is not known in Europe, although it does contain elements similar to ones found in Type 301, The Three Stolen Princesses.

The Japanese text employs the common euphemism daiji na

tokoro, *"important place," when referring to the female sex organs.*

• LONG AGO in a certain place there was a wealthy man with an only daughter who was very beautiful. It was decided that she should be married to a young man in a distant village. When the day for the marriage came, a splendid palanquin arrived from the bridegroom's village to carry the bride to her new home. The girl's mother and a great crowd of her relatives followed along after the palanquin calling, "The bride! The bride!" as they crossed over mountains and mountain passes. As they were going along a black cloud suddenly came from out of the sky and enveloped the bride's palanquin. When they saw this they began crying, "What shall we do? What shall we do?" But the black cloud snatched the bride from the palanquin, flew away with her, and disappeared.

The mother nearly became insane with worry about her daughter. "I must go and find her, no matter what happens," she said. Putting some cooked food in a pack on her back she set off, searching aimlessly about in the mountains.

She crossed fields and mountains, always searching and searching. Finally the sun began to set. Just then she saw a tiny temple in the distance. She went up to it and called, "I know that I look terrible, but could you please let me stay all night here, just for tonight." A priestess came from the temple and said, "I have nothing for you to sleep in and nothing for you to eat, but nevertheless you are welcome to stay." The mother entered the temple, and since she was so tired, she soon lay down to sleep. The priestess took off her own robe and spread it over the woman. Then she said, "Your daughter for whom you are searching is being held in the *oni* [malevolent ogre]'s mansion over across the river. There is a big dog and a little dog guarding there, so you cannot get across. Still, during the middle of the day, they sometimes take a nap, so you might be able to get across then. However, the bridge is an abacus bridge, and since there are many beads on it, you must be very careful how you step on it. If you miss one of the beads, you will fall through to the village of your birth; so do be careful."

The next morning the mother, surprised by a rustling noise, *sawa sawa,* suddenly woke up. There she found herself on a plain where reeds grew profusely. Neither the temple nor the priestess were to be seen. There were only the reeds moaning, *sawa sawa,* in the morning wind. The mother saw that she had been sleeping exposed to the wind and rain with only a stone monument for a pillow. "Thank you, priestess," she said and set off for the river bank as she had been told.

Just at that time the large dog and the small dog were taking a nap. Seeing that this was her chance, she carefully walked over the abacus bridge. Having crossed safely over the river, she went on and soon heard the familiar sound, *chan chan, chan karin,* of someone using a loom. Without thinking, the mother called, "Daughter!" The girl looked out the door; then the two of them ran and joyously embraced each other. The girl hurriedly cooked her mother some supper; then said, "It will be too bad for you if the *oni* finds you here," and she hid her in a stone chest.

Soon the *oni* came home. "It seems to me that it smells as if human beings are here," he said, sniffing, *kun kun,* with his nose. The girl said that she knew nothing about it, but the *oni* said, "If I look at the flower in the garden, I can tell."

Now there was a magical flower in the garden which always had just as many blossoms on it as there were human beings in the house. On this day there were three flowers in bloom, and the *oni* came back into the house in a great rage. "Where do you have those humans hidden?" he demanded, looking as if he were going to attack her at any moment. The girl wondered what she could possibly do. Suddenly an idea came to her. "I have become pregnant; perhaps that is why there are three flowers."

When he heard that, the *oni,* who had been so angry, suddenly was so overjoyed that he nearly stood on his head. In his joy he shouted to assemble his retainers saying, "Retainers, bring *sake* [rice wine] and drums; go and kill the dogs guarding the river!" And he danced around for joy. The retainers too were delighted and began shouting noisily: "Get the *sake,* get the drums! Kill the big dog, kill the little dog!"

Finally all the *oni* became drunk on the *sake* and fell asleep.

The *oni* general said, "Wife, I'm sleepy, show me where my wooden box is." The girl, upon hearing that he wanted his wooden box, was greatly relieved. She helped him get in it, then closed its seven lids and locked its seven locks. Hurriedly she got her mother from the stone box, and they fled from the *oni's* house.

Since the large dog and the small dog had been killed, there was nothing to worry about there, so they went to the storehouse where the vehicles were kept. "Shall we take a ten thousand *ri* [about 24,400 miles] chariot or a thousand *ri* chariot?" they asked one another, but just then the priestess came and said: "Neither the ten thousand *ri* chariot nor the thousand *ri* chariot will be any good. You should escape in the swift ship." The mother and her daughter got in the ship and fled away on the river as fast as they could.

The *oni,* asleep in the the wooden box, became thirsty and called, "Wife, bring me some water," but no matter how many times he called, there was no answer. He broke the seven lids off the box, got out and looked around, but the girl was not there. No matter where he looked, there was no trace of her at all. "Did that slut get away?" he cried. He jerked his retainers awake, and they went to the vehicle storehouse. They saw that the ship was gone, so they all went down to the river. There they could see the mother and her daughter just disappearing in the distance. "Drink up all the water in the river!" commanded the *oni* general, and all the whole crowd of *oni* immediately dropped down, stuck their heads in the water and *gabu gabu,* began drinking it up. Soon the water in the river began to fall, and the ship in which the mother and daughter were fleeing began to float back to where the *oni* were. It looked as though the *oni* would be able to reach out and grab them at any moment. The mother and daughter had already given up any hope of being saved, when just then the priestess appeared again. "Why are you here just doing nothing?" she asked. "Hurry, show your "important place" to the *oni!"*

The priestess joined them, and all three of them began rolling up their kimonos. When the *oni* saw that, they began to roar with laughter, *gera gera*. They rolled over and over in laughter and when they did that, all the water which they had drunk came up again and so the ship sailed off into the distance. In this way the mother and her daughter were saved from danger.

They thanked the priestess again and again, saying that this was all because of her help. The priestess said: "I am actually a stone monument. Every year please erect another monument beside me; that is what I will enjoy more than anything else." Then she disappeared from sight.

The mother and daughter were able to return home safely, and they never forgot their obligation to the priestess; every year they erected another stone monument for her.

•*17*• *Momotaro, The Peach Boy*

Motif T543.3, "Birth from a fruit," and the general motif G500, "Ogre defeated," are the main motifs found in this tale. Kata No. 159, "Momotaro 'Peach Boy.'" Collected in Sannohei-gun, Aomori-ken.

This tale has no analogues in European tradition but is one of the most popular stories in Japan, and the one most often reprinted in children's books. The Peach Boy is held up as an example of the combination of kindness, courage, and strength that Japanese boys are expected to achieve.

Tying a towel about one's head is often symbolic of the will to work hard at a task, as well as serving the purpose of absorbing sweat or blood from a wound. Momotaro's being given a new towel for his head symbolizes encouragement in striving hard to conquer the oni.

Momotaro's calling his foster parents "grandfather" and "grandmother" is an extension of the practice of children's referring to all elderly men and women as grandfather and grandmother.

Williams, p. 312, notes that the peach is supposed to have originated in China where it is an emblem of marriage and the symbol of immortality and springtime. This concept may have in-

*fluenced the use of the peach in Japanese stories of supernatural
birth. Cf. Tale No. 35, below, "The Old Man Who Made Flowers
Bloom," where a dog is born from a peach.*

• THIS WAS long ago. In a certain place lived an old man and his
wife. One day the old man went to the mountains to cut wood,
and the old woman went to the river to do her washing. As she
was doing the washing, a peach came floating, *tsunbura tsunbura,* down the river. The old woman plucked it from the water
and when she tasted it, found it to be delicious.

"This peach is so good, I'd like to take one to the old man
too," she thought and called out, "Good peaches come this way;
bad peaches go that way," and soon a large, delicious-looking
peach floated to where the old woman was. "This one looks
good," she cried and picking it up, carried it home and put it
in a cabinet.

When evening came, the old man returned home from the
mountains with a load of wood on his back. "Old woman, old
woman, I am home," he called.

"Old man, old man, I brought you a delicious peach today
from the river; here I've saved it for you to eat," and she brought
the peach from the cabinet.

Just as they put it on the cutting board to cut it open, it suddenly split apart; inside was a beautiful baby boy who began crying lustily, *hoogea hoogea,* waa waa.

The old man and his wife were overcome with surprise and
made a great to-do, crying, "Oh, oh, what shall we do?"

"Since he was born from the peach, let us name him Momotaro,
'Peach Boy,'" they said, and so they did. They raised him very
carefully, feeding him rice gruel and fish. He would eat one
bowlful and grow that much bigger, and if he ate two bowlfuls,
he would grow that much bigger. If he were taught to count to
one, he could remember all the numbers up to ten. He grew to
be a strong and intelligent boy. The old man and his wife loved
him and took great pleasure in caring for him.

One day Momotaro went to the old man and his wife. He sat
down on the floor in the formal style, with his hands on the
floor before him, and said, "Grandfather and grandmother, I am

grown now; I should like to go to the *Oni* Island and conquer the *oni*. Please make some of Japan's number-one *kibi dango* [pounded rice and millet dough] for me."

The old man and his wife replied, "Why do you ask to do this? You are not old enough; you could not defeat the *oni*." And they tried to dissuade him.

Momotaro, however, said, "I will defeat them," and would not be dissuaded; so the old man and the old woman could do nothing but agree. "Then you may go and do it," they said and made a great number of Japan's number-one *kibi dango*. They tied a new towel about his head and gave him new *hakama* [wide trousers]. They gave him a sword and a flag upon which was written, "Japan's Number-One Momotaro." Giving him a bag of the *kibi dango* to tie at his waist, they said: "Be careful. Go and return. We will wait for you until you have conquered the *oni*," and so despatched by the old man and his wife, Momotaro departed.

He went as far as the edge of the village when a dog came barking up to him, *wan wan,* bow wow. "Momotaro, Momotaro, where are you going?"

"I am going to the *Oni* Island to conquer the *oni*."

"Then I shall go to the *Oni* Island with you. Please give me one of those Japan's number-one *kibi dango*."

"You shall become my retainer. If you eat one of these, you will be as powerful as ten men," and he took one of the *dango* from the bag at his waist and gave it to the dog.

So the dog became his retainer, and they set off toward the mountains. Next a pheasant came flying, *ken ken,* up to them. He was given a *kibi dango* and became a retainer in the same way as the dog. Momotaro continued on to the mountains with his two retainers. Next a monkey came chattering up to them, *kya kya,* and he too became a retainer.

Momotaro became the general, the dog carried the flag, and they all hurried on to the *Oni* Island.

When they got to the *Oni* Island they could see a huge black gate. The monkey rapped, *don don,* on the door. From inside came a voice, "Who is there?" and a red *oni* came out.

Momotaro said, "I am Japan's number-one Momotaro. I have

come to conquer *Oni* Island; you had all better get ready," and pulling out his sword, he made ready to attack. The monkey took his long spear, the dog and the pheasant their swords, and all prepared to attack. The little *oni* at the gate set up an alarm and fled to the rear of the island. There all the *oni* were having a drinking party. When they heard that Momotaro was coming, they shouted, "Who is Momotaro, anyway?" and came out to fight.

Since the four had eaten Japan's number-one *kibi dango,* they had the strength of thousands of men, and so they defeated the whole *oni* force. The black *oni* general fell down in front of Momotaro, his hands on the ground and, with tears falling, *boro boro,* from his huge eyes, begged forgiveness, crying: "We are no match for you; please at least spare our lives. We will never do anything wrong again."

"Then from now on you must never do evil again. If you promise that, I shall spare your lives," said Momotaro.

"We will give you all our treasure," said the *oni* general and surrendered all the treasure that they had to Momotaro. Momotaro put the treasure in a cart and with the dog, monkey, and pheasant pulling, *enyara enyara,* heave ho, heave ho, he returned with it as a present for his grandfather and grandmother.

The old man and his wife were overjoyed and praised Momotaro greatly. The emperor heard of it, and Momotaro was given a great reward, with which he cared for the old man and his wife the rest of their days.

·18· The Dirt Boy

Type 301B, The Three Stolen Princesses, and cf. Type 513A, Six Go through the Whole World. Motif F601, "Extraordinary companions," is prominent here. Kata No. 157, "Riki-Taro, 'The Mighty Boy.'" Collected in Saraki-mura, Waga-gun, Iwate-ken, from Ushinosuke Hirano.

Thompson, p. 54, finds a resemblance between the extraordinary companions of this tale and those found in the eleventh-

century Mabinogion version of the King Arthur story. He states that the tale shows evidence of having come to Europe from India. There it is found not only in older Buddhistic writings but also in modern oral collections. Thompson and Roberts, p. 46, list eleven Indic variants. The antiquity of the Japanese tradition is attested to by a fragment found in the Kojiki, *an eighth-century Japanese history, pp. 167–68, where three strong men meet the legendary emperor, Jimmu. Ten oral versions have been recorded.*

The version of the tale given here is told as a local legend, and the place names given are those in the region around Waga-gun.

• LONG AGO in a certain place there were a very lazy old man and his wife. Every year, all year, they were covered with dirt. They had no children. "At our age, we have no more chance of having children; so let's take some of the dirt from our bodies and make a doll out of it," they said, and so they rubbed the dirt off their bodies. They got a great pile of it; then they made a boy out of it and named him Konbitaro, 'Dirt Boy.'

Konbitaro was a very hearty eater. If he were given one *sho* [about two quarts] of rice, he would eat it all, and if he were given one *to* [about four gallons] of rice, he would eat all of that; and so he grew very big and strong, until he could eat three *to* and five *sho* of rice all at one time.

The old man and his wife were very poor, and they began to complain that they could not afford to feed him that much rice. Konbitaro said: "Grandfather, grandfather, do not worry. I will go and practice physical training; please have a one-hundred-*kan* [about 800 pounds] iron stick made for me."

"What are you going to do with a hundred-*kan* iron stick?" asked the old man in surprise.

"I am going to use it for a walking stick," said the boy.

There was nothing else the old man could do; so he took his purse and emptied out what little money he had and gave it to a blacksmith to make a hundred-*kan* iron stick.

Konbitaro took the iron stick, and swinging it around and around his head with one hand, he bravely set off on his journey. He went merrily along and finally came to a place very similar to the Kameishi highway, where he saw a huge man coming toward him, huffing and puffing, *gishi gashi, gishi gashi,* as he carried a red temple, as big as the temple at Miyama Daigonken, on his back. Konbitaro took his iron stave and just barely poked the red temple. It immediately splintered to pieces. The man who was carrying the temple became very angry. "Do you know who I am? I am the strongest man in the world. I am Midokotaro, 'Red Temple Boy,'" and he sprang at Konbitaro, intending to show his strength by bending the iron stick. Konbitaro was prepared for him, and swinging the iron staff around and around, he hit Midokotaro and threw him into the air.

He waited and waited for him to come down, but he did not reappear. After a while he heard a voice crying from somewhere up in the air, "Help me, help me!" He looked up and saw that Midokotaro was caught in the top of a pine tree which was beside the road. There he was waving his arms about helplessly.

"There, do you give up?" said Konbitaro and pulled up the pine tree by the roots to rescue Midokotaro.

"I am no match for you. Please take me as your retainer," said Midokotaro; and so he became Konbitaro's retainer. After this they went along until they came to a rock quarry, similar to the one at the pass at Sennin Nagane. There they saw a huge man breaking rocks, *gagin gagin,* bang, crash, with the palm of his hand.

By chance a big piece of rock came flying toward Konbitaro. He opened his mouth and, with a blast of his breath, he blew the rock back in the opposite direction. It hit the rock-breaker with a thud, *gokin,* right in the face. The man became angry and cried: "Who are you? Who is this fellow who dares to throw rocks at me. I am Ishikotaro, 'Rock Boy,' the strongest man in the world." Red with anger, he charged toward them.

"We shall see who is the strongest in the world," said Konbitaro. Then he said to Midokotaro, "Go and fight with him."

Midokotaro immediately obeyed and began to fight as hard as he could with Ishikotaro. They fought this way and that, but neither could win. "Then I shall fight. Midokotaro, you stand over there," said Konbitaro, and he took his place in the fight. He grabbed Ishikotaro by the neck and threw him down with all his might. Ishikotaro landed in the pile of quarry waste rock and was buried up to his neck.

After this Ishikotaro also became his retainer, and Konbitaro, accompanied by his two retainers, went along until he came to a castle town similar to the one at Osawa. However, even though it was midday, there wasn't a single house open in the whole town, and not a person was to be seen. When they came to what appeared to be the house of the richest man in the town, they saw a beautiful young girl all alone, crying and sobbing. "What are you crying about, young girl?" they asked.

"Every month on the first day of the month a frightful *bakemono* comes from the nearby village and takes one of the girls from the town. Today it is my turn to be taken, and that is why I am crying."

"All right, all right, then we three will capture that monster," they said, and Konbitaro was taken by the girl into the mansion.

He told the people in the mansion to put the girl in a brass chest; then he posted Midokotaro in the garden and Ishikotaro at the door of the house. Konbitaro himself sat down in the room in front of the brass chest to wait for the *bakemono*.

After a while night fell. Soon the *bakemono* came, calling out in a loud voice, "Where is my bride? If she has run off, I will roast her and eat her." The *bakemono's* voice sounded like a cracked temple bell, and he was so tall that if he had been inside the mansion his head would have stuck out through the roof.

As he entered the garden, Midokotaro attacked him, but as soon as the *bakemono* saw him, he picked him up and swallowed him whole. When he got to the door of the mansion, Ishikotaro attacked him, but picking him up with the tip of his fingers, the *bakemono* swallowed him too.

Seeing that the two retainers had been swallowed whole, Konbitaro became very angry and began whirling the iron stick around and around. "Now I shall fight with you," he cried and attacked the *bakemono*.

The *bakemono* began fighting back, and after a while he grabbed the iron stick in the middle and began to twist it. Konbitaro threw the iron stick away and began to fight the *bakemono* with his hands. They fought and fought, but neither of them could win; then it began to look dangerous for Konbitaro. Konbitaro knew that he would have to do something so he suddenly kicked the *bakemono* right in the testicles, which were as big as a four *to* [about 16 gallons] *sake* barrel. The *bakemono,* strong as he was, had been hit in a vital spot. Blowing Midokotaro out of his right nostril and Ishikotaro out of his left, he fell over dead.

When the people of the house saw what had happened, they all came out of hiding. "You have saved our daughter and us too! What would you like as a reward?" they cried, clapping their hands for joy.

The three men said that they needed no reward, except that they would like to have some rice. The people took a five *to* [about 20 gallons] kettle usually used for boiling hemp and filled it with rice; then gave it to the three men to eat. After they had eaten it, the people said: "You three have wanted nothing from us, but we would still like to reward you. Even though they are not worthy of men such as you, please take our daughters in marriage."

To Konbitaro they gave the eldest daughter, the one whom he had rescued. They gave their other daughters to the other two men. Konbitaro brought his old grandfather and grandmother from his home village and took good care of them for as long as they lived.

Dondo hare. "With this, it's sold out."

·*19*· *The Three Lucky Charms*

Motif D672, "Obstacle flight," is the principle motif involved here. Kata No. 75, "The Three Lucky Charms." Collected in Asamai-mura, Hiraka-gun, Akita-ken, from collector Denichiro Terada's grandfather.

Twenty-six versions of this tale have been collected in Japan. The motif of magic flight has a wide distribution in Japan, one of the earliest occurrences being in the Kojiki, *p. 39, where Izanami, one of the creators of the country of Japan, flees from* and eludes an ogress when a vine headdress is transformed into grapes and a comb into bamboo sprouts. The ogress stops to eat the grapes and bamboo sprouts, allowing Izanami to escape.

The cluster of motifs which makes up the obstacle-flight motif appears throughout the world. This was the subject of the final monograph in the long career of the well-known Finnish folklorist, Antti Aarne. None of the Japanese examples of the motif, however, were available to him when the study was made in 1930.

• AUTUMN HAD come and in the mountains the chestnuts were getting red. The boys of the village decided to go out chestnut gathering. The young acolyte in the temple wanted to go too and said, "Priest-*san*, priest-*san*, may I please go and gather chestnuts too."

The priest said, "My boy, my boy, there are old *oni* women in the mountains; so it would be better not to go." But the acolyte wanted to go so badly that he could not bear it, and he said, "But priest-*san*, I still want to go." And he begged so hard that the priest finally said: "All right, you may go since you want to so badly. I will give you three valuable charms. If there is ever anything you need, you may ask the charms for it."

The acolyte took the charms and set off for the mountains, thinking that he would collect a lot of chestnuts before dark. When he got to the mountains, he began picking up chestnuts as fast as he could, and while he was doing this, it gradually began to get dark. The wind began to blow, *go-o go-o*, and an old *oni* woman came out. She took the acolyte with her to her house. The acolyte was very frightened, but there was nothing he could do. After a while he became sleepy and went to bed.

In the middle of the night rain began to fall. It started leaking through the roof, making this song as it fell,

> *Dara zugu, dara zugu, datta,*
> Drip, drip, splatter, splatter,
> Get up and look at the old woman's face.

The acolyte heard what the dripping rain water said and opened his eyes. He saw that the old woman had her mouth open one *shaku* [about one foot] wide in an evil grimace and was blackening her teeth. He was sure that the *oni* woman intended to eat him up, and he began crying, "Grandmother, grandmother, I have to pass a stool."

"Do it there in the corner of the fireplace," she said.

"An acolyte doesn't go around doing it in the fireplace."

"Then do it in the storeroom."

"An acolyte doesn't go around doing it in the storeroom," he said.

"Oh, what a bother you are! All right, I'll tie a rope on you and let you go to the toilet," and she tied a heavy rope around his waist and let him go to the toilet.

When he got to the toilet the acolyte knew that this was his chance to escape. He took the rope from his waist and tied it to a pillar, then took out one of the lucky charms he had been given by the priest and asked it to answer when his name was called; then he fled from the old *oni* woman's house.

The acolyte didn't return and didn't return, and the *oni* woman called out, "Aren't you done yet, boy?" The lucky charm in the toilet answered, "Not yet, not yet." No matter how often the *oni* woman called, the charm would answer, "Not yet, not yet," and the acolyte never returned.

"What a slow one you are!" cried the old woman and jerked on the rope. The pillar in the toilet rattled, *gata gata*. "Oh, so you've run away!" she cried and started off in pursuit, running in her bare feet.

The acolyte ran on and on through the pitch-dark mountains. After a while he could hear the old *oni* woman coming in pursuit, calling, "Acolyte, where are you?" Soon it looked as though she were going to catch him. He took out another one of the lucky charms and cried, "Make a big sand mountain"; then he threw it down. In an instant a mountain of sand appeared behind him. The old *oni* woman tried to climb it, and it broke away; she tried again, and it crumbled beneath her; in this way the acolyte escaped again. He continued on, crossing valleys and mountains. After a while it again looked as though the old *oni* woman would catch him.

"Make a great wide river," he cried, throwing down another

lucky charm. In an instant a wide river appeared. The old *oni*
woman tried to swim across it but was washed away; she tried
again and was washed away, and in the meantime the acolyte
escaped again.

Finally the acolyte reached the temple. He pounded on the
kitchen door, crying, "Priest-*san*, priest-*san*, I am being pursued
by an old *oni* woman; hurry, open the door."

The priest was sleeping. He woke up and replied: "You see,
that is why I told you that you shouldn't go to the mountains.
Wait until I tie up my gee string."

"Hurry up! Hurry up! If you don't hurry, the old *oni* woman
will eat me up!"

"Wait until I get my kimono on," said the priest. Then, "Wait
until I tie my sash." Then, "Wait until I put on my sandals."
Then, "Wait until I get my cane." Finally after he was all ready,
he opened the door.

"The old *oni* woman is coming now, please save me!" cried
the acolyte and ran into the house. The priest took out a huge
bamboo trunk and put the acolyte in it; then he hung it from
the ceiling and went about his business as if nothing had happened.

Soon the old *oni* woman came running up to the house.
"Priest-*san*, priest-*san*, did the acolyte come here?"

"No, he didn't. No, he didn't."

"Now, priest-*san*, he must have come here," she said. Then she
noticed the bamboo trunk hanging from the ceiling. "There,
priest-*san*, open that up," she demanded.

"If you will do what I tell you to, I will open it up and show it
to you," he said.

"Grow taller, grow taller," he said and gradually the old *oni*
woman grew tall enough so that she could almost reach the bamboo trunk. Then the priest said, "grow shorter, grow shorter,"
and the old *oni* woman grew smaller and smaller until the priest
had her as small as he wanted, down to the size of a bean; then
he took one of the pieces of *mochi* which was roasting by the
fireplace, wrapped her in it, and swallowed her in one gulp.

He took the acolyte down from the ceiling and warned him
never again to refuse to listen to what he was told. Soon after

this the priest's stomach began to hurt. He went to the toilet, and a great number of flies came out of his anus. The *oni* old woman had turned into flies, and they spread throughout all Japan.

•20• *The* Oni *and the Three Children*

Type 327A, Hansel and Gretel. Kata No. 82B, "Kozuna, the Oni's Child." Collected in Kami Kuishiki-mura, Nishi Yatsu-shiro-gun, Yamanashi-ken, from Tsume Kono.

This tale is widely distributed in Japan, with some sixty-seven examples recorded. While in the version of the tale given here it is the real mother, not the stepmother, who abandons the children, most Japanese versions have the stepmother as the villain. Cruel stepmother tales are as popular in Japan as they are in Europe.

Thompson, p. 37, notes that the whole complex of tales about children and ogres seems to be European, although the elements are often simple enough to have been independently invented elsewhere. The fact that the tale is very widespread in Japan and lacks a number of the motifs found in the European tradition suggests that the tale as it is found in Japan may well be indigenous there.

• THERE WAS once a very poor family. The father had died long ago and the mother was left with three boys, the oldest one being eleven. The younger ones were nine and seven years old. The mother found it very difficult to provide for them all.

The mother said to herself: "Here I am, just one lone woman. Though I work as hard as I can, I hardly earn enough to keep myself alive; I just cannot provide enough to raise my children properly. It is a terrible thing to have to see them suffer; it would be much better to take them to the mountains and abandon them. If an animal came along and ate them up, at least they would not have to suffer." The mother kept thinking like this until finally she decided to abandon them in the mountains.

One day she took the three children far back in the mountains with her. "You wait here for me a little while," said she; "I am going to go and buy you some sweetmeats to eat." And so she left them there and returned home.

The children believed what she told them and waited and waited until it became dark, but their mother did not return. Finally, unable to bear it any longer, the two older boys began crying.

"Brothers, it won't do any good to cry," said the youngest child, who was only seven; "there must be a house around here somewhere in which we can find a place to stay. Here, I'll climb up a tree and see if I can find one," and he climbed a nearby tree. From up in the tree he could see the light of a fire, far off in the distance. "There! Over there I can see a fire. Let's go!"

The youngest boy climbed down from the tree. Encouraging his brothers to accompany him, he set off in the direction of the light. They went along until finally they came to a dilapidated little hut in the middle of the mountains. In the hut an old woman sat alone by the fireplace in which she had built a big fire.

The boys entered the hut and said, "We have lost our way and do not know what to do. Could you please let us stay here just for tonight?"

"I would like to let you stay, but this house is an *oni* house. The *oni* will be coming home any time now, and so I can't let you stay here. If you leave by this road, you will meet the *oni*, but if by that road, you can avoid meeting him. Now I think you'd better leave."

The boys did not want to leave and begged again saying: "Even if the *oni* is coming back, it is so dark now that we can't go any further. Please let us stay here someway or other, just for one night."

"If the *oni* comes now he will catch you all and eat you. Is that what you want?" said the old woman. And then even while she was talking, the sound of the *oni's* footsteps could be heard, *zushin zushin,* as he approached the hut.

"There! I told you so!" cried the old woman, becoming frightened. "You've been dawdling around and here the *oni* is coming. What shall I do! Here, hurry, get in here," and she put them down in an underground storage pit, shut the lid tightly, and covered it with a straw mat.

Just then the *oni* came in through the back door. Immediately he began sniffing the air, *fusu fusu,* sniff sniff, and cried: "Old woman, it smells as if human beings have been here. There must be somebody staying here," and he began searching through the whole house.

The old woman was very worried and said: "Just now three boys came by and wanted to stay overnight, but they heard you coming and became frightened and ran away. That must be what you smell; the odor of the boys must still be here."

"If there were three boys here, I've got to catch them. Since they just left, I'll soon get them. Look out! Look out!" He drew on his "Thousand *Ri* [2,440 miles] in One Step" boots and shot out of the front door like a bullet.

But no matter how he ran after the boys, he could not find them at all. "Well, perhaps I've run too far. They will surely be coming by here; I'll just lie down and rest a little." So he sat down by the road to rest. He became sleepy and was soon snoring, *guu guu.*

As soon as the *oni* left, the old woman took the three boys out of the storage pit and said: "The *oni* has put on his 'Thousand *Ri* in One Step' boots, and so he must be far from here by now. You'd better take this road here and escape as fast as you can," and she sent the children out of the back door.

They ran along for a long ways and came to a place where it sounded as if the thunder deity lived. A loud noise, *goo goo,* was coming from somewhere. Wondering what it was, they went along and saw the huge *oni* lying on the bank across the road, asleep and snoring. The children were so frightened that the two older boys began crying and sobbing, *shiku shiku.* "Brothers, it won't do any good to cry. If the *oni* is sleeping soundly, we can sneak by him," said the youngest boy.

The youngest brother softly crept up to where the *oni* was sleeping. The *oni* was sound asleep and snoring loudly. The boy happened to glance at the *oni*'s feet and said to himself, "Those are surely the 'Thousand *Ri* in One Step' boots. I would like to get them in some way or other," and softly, so as not to wake the *oni,* he began to pull the boots off. He finally got one off, and just then the *oni* moved his foot suddenly and turned over in his sleep. The boy was surprised and held his breath. The *oni* began talking in his sleep. "Those mice must be out night-prowl-ing again," he said.

The boy waited until the *oni* had become quiet again, and then he slipped the other boot off. The *oni* again moved his foot and turned over in his sleep. The boy held his breath again while the *oni* muttered in his sleep, "Those mice must have come back again," but he soon went sound asleep again.

As soon as the boy saw that the *oni* was asleep again, he took both the boots and hurried back to where his brothers were. "Older brother, hurry, put these on!" he cried and gave the boots to the oldest child. The boy put them on and tied the two younger brothers to his back; then the youngest boy cried, "Now, fly!" and suddenly the three brothers went whistling through the air, *zushi zushi,* zing zing, like a rifle bullet.

Soon the *oni* woke up. "Those wretched boys got away from me!" he cried, and gnashing his teeth in disgust, he set out after the children. However, since the "Thousand *Ri* in One Step" boots had been taken from him, he could not catch up with them. The children soon reached a place where people lived, and so there was nothing the *oni* could do but return home. When the old woman saw the *oni* coming, she was worried about the children and tried to find out if he had caught them.

"I chased after them a little too far, and while I was resting someone stole my boots, and so I couldn't catch them," he re-plied. When she heard this the old woman was greatly relieved.

The three boys returned home safely, and after that they worked very hard and helped their mother.

•21• *The Golden Chain from Heaven*

Type 333, The Glutton (Red Ridinghood). *Kata No. 80, "The Sky Deity's Golden Chain." Collected in Higashi Iyayama-mura, Mima-gun, Tokushima-ken, from Kozo Nakano.*

Japanese variants of this tale usually follow the plot of Type 123, The Wolf and the Kids, more closely than they do Red Ridinghood, except that the actors in the Japanese tradition are always human rather than animal. The famous Walt Disney animation of "The Three Little Pigs" contains many of the motifs usually found in Japanese variants of the tale given here.

Thirty texts have been recorded in Japan, chiefly in southern districts. A good version is found in Zong In-sob's Folktales From Korea, pp. 7–10, and Eberhard, pp. 19–21, gives reference to some forty-five Chinese variants.

Most ogres in Japanese tales are more impulsive than clever and can be easily hoodwinked. However, they are frightening and may cause their victims to act irrationally. The yamauba would have had no chance of catching the boys had she not frightened them into telling her how to climb the tree, but it was her impulsive use of the rotten rope that brought about her destruction.

• VERY, VERY long ago, there lived a father and mother and three children. When the youngest child was still small, the father died. On the seventh day after his death, the mother went to visit his grave and left the three children to look after the house.

"In these mountains here, there is a frightful old *yamauba* [malevolent ogress]. While I am gone, even if someone comes, do not open the door," said the mother; then she left.

After a short while the *yamauba* came. "Your mother has returned now," she called out.

"Then put out your hand; let us see," said the children. She stuck out her hand, and they saw that it was covered with hair. "Our mother's hands are much smoother than that. You are a *yamauba*," they said.

The *yamauba* went somewhere, borrowed a razor, and shaved the rough hair off her hand. She took some buckwheat flour and smoothed her hands, then came back to the children's house again. "Your mother has returned now," she called.

"Then let us see your hand," the children said. The *yamauba* stuck out her hand and the children felt of it. It was very nice and smooth, but the *yamauba*'s breathing was very rough and her voice sounded like someone rolling kettles down a mountain canyon. "Our mother has a much nicer voice than you," said the boys.

The *yamauba* went and drank some water in which red beans had been washed; then she came back and knocked, *ton ton,* on the door. "Your mother is late, but she has finally returned," she called out.

This time the *yamauba*'s voice was just like their mother's, and the boys thought that it must really be she; so they opened the door, and the *yamauba,* disguised as their mother, came into the house.

When they went to bed the two older boys slept in one room as usual, and the youngest boy slept with the disguised *yamauba* mother in an adjoining room. About the middle of the night, as the two older boys were sleeping, they heard a sound, *kori kori,* crunch, crunch, coming from the next room. "Mother, what are you eating?" they called.

"I am eating pickles," replied the *yamauba* mother.

"Please give us one," they begged, and she tore the fingers from one of the child's hands and threw them to the older boys. They picked them up and saw that it was their little brother's fingers; then they realized for the first time that this was the *yamauba*. Softly the two boys got up, took a jar of oil, and left the house. They climbed up in the tree by the gate and poured the oil down the tree trunk.

As soon as the *yamauba* discovered that the two boys had escaped, she ran after them. When she got to the pond by the front gate, she saw the reflection of the boys in the water. She went and got a net and tried to scoop them up out of the water, but she could not do it. By chance she happened to look up and saw the boys up in the tree. She tried to climb up after them, but she kept slipping back down the tree. "How shall I get up in the tree?" she screamed, and the boys became so frightened that they told her to cut notches in the tree. The *yamauba* went to the storeroom and got a sickle. Cutting notches in the tree, she climbed up toward the boys.

The two brothers became so frightened that they didn't know

what to do. They prayed, "Deity of the sky, let down an iron chain or something!" Immediately from up in the sky a golden chain descended, *suru suru,* smoothly down to where they were. They grabbed hold of the chain and climbed up it.

When the *yamauba* saw that she prayed, "Deity of the sky, let down a chain or a rope," and immediately a rotten rope came down. The *yamauba* grabbed the rotten rope and started to climb up to the sky, but the rope broke and she fell to the ground.

When she fell her blood gushed out and flowed onto a buckwheat plant that was nearby. It is said that the roots of buckwheat are red now because of what happened then. The brothers climbed on up into the sky; there the older brother became the moon and the younger brother a star.

•22• *The Swamp* Nushi's *Messenger*

Motif K511, "Uriah letter changed," is the major motif found in this tale. Kata No. 168, "The Swamp Deity's Letter." Collected in Yonesato-mura, Esashi-gun, Iwate-ken, from Toshizo Asakura.

The theme of the Uriah Letter appears in many ancient literary works, such as the Iliad *of Homer, in collections of Buddhistic myths, and in the Biblical story of David and Bathsheba, the source from which the motif derives its name.*

The tale as given here is found chiefly in northern Japan where nineteen versions have been collected; three additional variants have been recorded in other parts of the country. Dorson, in Folk Legends of Japan, *pp. 121–22, gives a legend about a snake goddess who inhabited a pond. He also presents a legend about horses and swamps, pp. 164–66.*

The Grand Shrines at Ise are the oldest and most important of Shinto shrines. The devout aspire to make a pilgrimage to these shrines at least once during their lifetime.

• THIS IS A tale about the Mizouke swamp. At the edge of the swamp there lived a farmer named Magojiro. A large group of people from the village decided to make a pilgrimage to Ise, but

Magojiro, complaining, "I'm so poor I can't go at all," continued to go to the edge of the swamp every day and cut grass.

One day a beautiful lady came up out of the swamp and called to Magojiro: "You have been cutting the grass from around the swamp every day like this, year after year, and I would like to repay you for it. Isn't there anything you would like?"

Now Magojiro was rather slow-witted. When the woman appeared and spoke to him he thought it nothing unusual and said, "I want to go to Ise on the pilgrimage, but I have no money and so I can't go."

The woman smiled and said: "Oh, that is easy; I'll give you some money so you can go. In exchange for that, I have a little request I'd like to make of you. Will you please take this letter to the Taka swamp near the plains at the foot of Mt. Fuji. When you get to that swamp, clap your hands and a woman will appear. She is my younger sister; please give this letter to her. Here is some money." And the woman handed Magojiro the letter and a bag of money.

Magojiro took the money he had received from the swamp *nushi* [ogress] and set off on the pilgrimage. Everyone in the group wondered how it was that he was able to make the pilgrimage. They continued on for many days, stopping each night, and finally arrived at the plains at the foot of Mt. Fuji. Magojiro secretly left the company of pilgrims and went to the swamp there. On the way he met a *rokubu* [itinerant ascetic] who asked, "What are you going to this swamp for?" Magojiro took out the letter and showed it to him. The *rokubu* read it and was shocked to see what was written there.

The letter said: "Every day this man comes and cuts the grass around my swamp. As the days pass it is getting more and more difficult to hide myself. I would like to capture him and eat him up, but if I did, everyone would naturally know that there was a swamp *nushi* here, and I would have more difficulties. I am sending him to you. Please take him and eat him up."

"We must rewrite this letter," said the *rokubu*. He took out his ink and brush and rewrote it to read: "This man has been cutting the grass around my swamp for me every year for many years; so I would like to reward him in some way. Please give him something if you can. I think that perhaps a gold horse would be the best thing."

After he had rewritten the letter, the *rokubu* gave it to Magojiro, who then set off for the swamp. He clapped his hands as he had been told by the swamp woman at his home, and a beautiful woman came up out of the swamp. She read the letter that Magojiro handed her and a look of suspicion crossed her face, but she invited Magojiro to enter the swamp with her.

"I can't do that, I never get into water," said Magojiro. But the woman said, "I will take you on my back, all you need to do is close your eyes," and so Magojiro did as the woman told him. Finally the woman said, "Now you may open your eyes," and when he did he found himself in the middle of a splendid sitting room. Everything around was of the most exquisite beauty.

No matter how pleasant everything was, after he had been there for what seemed about three days, Magojiro said that he would like to go home. As he was departing, the swamp woman, as had been requested in the letter, brought a horse from the barn and gave it to him. "If you give this horse one cup of rice a day, he will drop a nugget of gold for you," she said.

Magojiro mounted the horse, and before he knew it, he was already at Ise. In a short time he made his pilgrimage to the shrines, and then just as soon as he got on the horse again, he was already back in his own country. Just as he was approaching the village, he caught up with the rest of the villagers who had been on the pilgrimage. It had been just one hundred days since he had left them, and now he was returning with them.

Magojiro tied the horse at the rear of his house. Every day he would give it a cup of rice, and every day the horse would drop a nugget of gold from his anus. In no time at all, Magojiro had become a happy and prosperous *choja*.

Now it happened that among Magojiro's brothers, there was one who was a worthless fellow. He wondered how his dull-witted older brother had suddenly become so rich. One day he secretly went into the house and saw that a splendid horse was tied there whose dung dropped out as nuggets of gold. Thinking this very strange, he gave the horse the cup of rice which was there, and a nugget of gold came out. "So this is it," thought the younger brother, and he decided to make the horse give a lot of gold at once. He rushed out and got more than one *to* [about 50 pounds] of rice and fed it to the horse. The horse was suddenly filled with energy and, whinnying loudly, flew to the mountain on the boundary between Rikuchu and Arita, and he stuck there. That is said to be the place now called Kamagagoku, 'Horse Mountain.'

Part III
Supernatural
Husbands or Wives

·23· The Woman Who Came Down from Heaven

Type 313 Ib, IIb, The Girl as Helper in the Hero's Flight; *cf. Type 400,* The Man on a Quest for his Lost Wife, *and Type 465A,* The Quest for the Unknown. *The principal motifs are D361.1, "The swan maiden," and H310, "Son-in-law tasks." Also in this text and in Dorson,* Folk Legends of Japan, *pp. 225–27, appears Motif K1335, "Seduction (or wooing) by stealing clothes of bathing girl (swan maiden)." Kata No. 149, "The Wife from the Upper World." Collected on Kakeroma Island, Oshima-gun, Kagoshima-ken, from Shomu Nobori.*

The swan maiden motif is world-wide. In literary tradition it appears in The Thousand and One Nights *and forms one of the poems of the Old Norse* Edda. *For Japan, Ikeda, p. 89, notes that the oldest recorded version is found in the eighth-century* Fudoki, *a collection of local records compiled by Imperial order in A.D. 712. A strikingly beautiful Noh drama,* Hagoromo ("Feather Robe"), *incorporates the swan maiden motif.*

The motif of the son-in-law tasks, too, is widespread throughout the world. It is very old in Japan, being found in the eighth-century historical and mythological record, the Kojiki, *pp. 86–88, where it is an episode in the story of Okuninushi, one of the mythical founders of the Japanese nation.*

The tale incorporating the two motifs is popular in Japanese oral tradition, with forty-six versions recorded. The Manyoshu, Book Eight, Part Two, *contains a poem attributed to the eighth century which has as its theme the reunion of the two lovers as stars.*

The hifukidake [bamboo mouth bellows] is often endowed with magical properties, since with it one can create a large fire from a tiny spark. Concealing the note in the bellows may have lent efficacy to the message through contagious magic.

The seventh day of the seventh month, July 7th, is celebrated as the Tanabata *festival to observe the one-day reunion of the two lovers. Bamboo trees are decorated with gay paper streamers*

*on which poems are written, and children receive special treats
and favors.*

*The importance in Japan of ritualized cleanliness in connec-
tion with spiritual or magical phenomena is illustrated by the dis-
appearance of the child's heavenly stipend of rice after the river
had been polluted.*

• IN A CERTAIN place there once lived a young man named
Mikeran. Every day he would go out to work in the fields or to
the mountains to cut firewood, and thus he made his living.

One day he went with the rest of the villagers to the mountains to cut firewood. As they were working in the mountains,
they would often go to the stream which flowed nearby to get a
drink or to wash the sweat from their bodies. On this day,
Mikeran finished his work earlier than usual and went down to
the stream to wash and get a drink. He decided to go farther
upstream than the pool where the villagers usually went. Going
along, he came to a large marsh where hardly anyone had ever
been.

Mikeran took off his sweat-soaked clothes and was just about
to dive into the water when he happened to glance up at a pine
tree which grew at the edge of the pool. There he saw a beautiful kimono hanging on one of the branches of the tree.

"Ah, what a beautiful kimono," he cried, and immediately
took it from the branch where it was hanging. Just as he took
the kimono, a woman came up out of the pool. Joining her
hands in supplication, she cried: "That is my flying kimono;
it is a feather robe and is of no use to human beings. Please give
it back to me."

Mikeran, however, made no answer; he merely stood staring at
the woman.

"Mikeran, did you not understand my request. That kimono
is mine. Unless I have it, I cannot return to heaven. You are a
human being and a flying kimono is of no use to you; please
give it back to me." The woman, begging with all her heart, re-
peated her request.

"What are you doing here?" asked Mikeran and again refused to return the kimono.

The woman thought perhaps that if she told him the real reason why she was there, he might not think it so strange and would return her kimono. With tears rolling down her cheeks she began: "From time to time, I come down from heaven to bathe here. I am a woman from heaven and not a woman who lives in this world. If you doubt me, please give back my robe, and you shall see."

Mikeran still refused to grant her request. "You must return to the island with me," he said. "We shall become friends and live together as man and wife. Then you will not need to come all the way down from heaven just to bathe here, but I shall bring you here whenever you want."

"Oh, Mikeran, please do not say such things!" cried the woman. "I am a woman from heaven; I cannot live with people of this earth. Please, please give me back my robe."

"No, no," replied Mikeran. "If I were to return your kimono, you would immediately return to heaven. Come home with me and let us be friends," and Mikeran absolutely refused to return the kimono.

The woman was filled with sorrow; but since Mikeran would not give back her kimono, she could not return to heaven, and so she went with him to his village and became his wife.

After this, seven years passed and three children were born, but the woman still longed with all her heart to return to heaven. Not knowing where her kimono was hidden, she kept hunting everywhere for it.

One day when her husband had gone fishing, the woman strapped the youngest child, who was still a baby, onto the back of the oldest child, who was seven. She asked the five-year-old child to pat the baby on the back. Having asked the older children to take care of the baby, she went to draw water from the river some distance from the village. She soon returned and, approaching the front gate, heard the children behind the house singing a lullaby to the baby:

> Bye, bye, baby, do not cry.
> When father returns, there's a surprise.
> He'll open the storehouse,
> The four and six pillar storehouse,

And in behind the millet bags,
Down behind the rice bags,
There is the feather robe.
There is the dancing robe;
He'll take it out for us.

The woman, hearing the children's song, had found out at last that the feather kimono, which she had hunted for seven long years, lay hidden under the rice and millet bags in the storehouse. Before her husband could return home, she took a ladder, climbed up to the double doors of the high storehouse, opened them, and went in. She searched among the bags of millet and rice and soon found the kimono.

Before her husband could come home, she immediately put the oldest child on her back, the second child inside the bosom of her kimono, and the youngest in her right arm. Wearing the feather kimono, she waved her arms once and rose above the top of the pine tree in the garden. She waved her arms a second time and rose above the highest clouds in the sky. The third time she waved her arms she alighted in heaven, but sadly enough, just as she was making the last flight from the top of the clouds, the baby which she was holding in her arm slipped and fell from her hands.

When Mikeran returned from fishing, he went into the house, but no one was there. Not only was the house empty, the door of the storehouse had been left open. "The feather robe has been discovered," he thought to himself, "and now it is gone."

He sat down, lost in thought, but finally realized that it was near supper time. He went over to the fireplace and began to build a fire. He took up the *hifukidake* [bamboo mouth bellows] and tried to blow up the fire, but no air would come through it. Knowing that something was the matter, he looked inside the bamboo stick and saw a piece of paper folded up and stuck inside. Pulling the paper out he unfolded it and read:

Gather a thousand pairs of wooden clogs and a thousand pairs of straw sandals. Bury them in the earth and plant a bamboo tree above them. Wait two or three years until the bamboo has grown up to heaven; then you will be able to climb up into heaven with no trouble at all.

Mikeran immediately set to work collecting wooden clogs and straw sandals, but try as he might, he could find only nine hundred and ninety-nine pairs of each. However, he buried them and planted a bamboo tree above them. The bamboo began to grow, and soon three years passed. It now looked as though the bamboo reached clear up to heaven, and Mikeran, filled with happiness, began his ascent. He climbed and climbed, but just as he was nearing heaven, with only a short way to go, he came to the tiptop of the bamboo tree. He was unable to get into heaven and remained in the top of the tree, swaying back and forth in the breeze.

The woman had returned to her place in heaven, but she still occasionally thought about the things she had left on earth. She would sit at her loom in the weaving room and look down below. As she watched the bamboo tree grow, she waited with eagerness the time when it would reach heaven.

One day, when she was sitting at her loom as usual, she looked out of her window and saw, down below, that the bamboo tree had reached almost to heaven. The top of the tree was just below her, waving in the breeze. She looked closely and saw, clinging to the topmost branch of the tree, a man who looked as small as a poppy seed.

The woman was overjoyed at seeing him. She took the shuttle from her loom and slowly lowered it until it was just above Mikeran's head. He grasped the shuttle, and she pulled him up into heaven.

After Mikeran got into heaven the woman's mother treated him very kindly, but her father requested him to do many very difficult things.

Just at that time it was the season in heaven for preparing the fields for planting. The woman's father commanded Mikeran to go to the mountains and clear one thousand *chobu* [about 2,500 acres] of land in one day. Mikeran, knowing that such a thing was completely impossible, did not know what to do. While he was wondering what he might do, the woman came and said to him, "When you go to clear the one thousand *chobu* of land, you must cut down three large trees, and using the stumps as a pillow, go to sleep a while."

The next morning when Mikeran went to the mountains as he had been commanded by the woman's father, he did as the woman had told him, and he was able to clear off all the trees in one day.

He returned and reported to the woman's father that the field was cleared. But this was not the end. Her father said, "Now you must spade up the whole field in one day."

Mikeran was greatly troubled, for he knew that he could never accomplish such a task in one day. But while he was worrying about what to do, the woman came to him and said, "This is easy; you must go to the field, turn up three clumps of dirt with the hoe, and, using them as a pillow, lie down and sleep for a while. In no time at all, it will all be spaded for you."

Mikeran did as he had been instructed, and soon the field was all spaded. He happily returned home, and when he told the woman's father that he had finished the work, her father said, "Now you must plant winter melons in the whole one thousand *chobu* field which you spaded yesterday," and thus he was given another difficult task.

This, too, was much more than he could ever do in one day, so Mikeran again had a talk with the woman. "You must plant melon seeds in three places, then lie down and go to sleep for a while," she instructed. "If you do this, the whole one thousand *chobu* field will soon be planted to melons." He did as he was told, and so the melons were all planted in one day.

Thinking that this would surely be the end of the work, Mikeran returned to the woman's father, who immediately said, "Tomorrow you must gather all the ripe melons from the seeds you have just planted and bring them all to me."

Mikeran thought that such a thing would be completely impossible; he wondered how the melon vines could grow and bloom and the melons ripen in just one night. He was very discouraged, but again the woman came to him and said: "You need not worry; the melons have already bloomed and are now ripe. All you need do is pick three of them and lie down using them as a pillow, and everything will be done for you."

Mikeran thought that what the woman told him was certainly

a very strange thing, but early the next morning he went out to the field, and there were all the melons, already ripe and ready to be gathered, just as the woman had said. He did as he had been instructed to do, and so all the melons from the one thousand *chobu* field were soon gathered, and he happily returned home.

Since Mikeran had accomplished this last task without incident, the woman's father was very pleased, and preparations were made for a harvest festival.

Mikeran was appointed to take care of serving the melons for the feast. The woman's father, who until then had treated him very harshly, now kindly instructed him how to cut the melons. "You must take three melons," he said. "Cut them lengthwise; then, lying face upward on them, go to sleep."

The woman, who was sitting nearby, signaled with her eyes to Mikeran, "You must not do as my father says but cut them crosswise." Mikeran felt that he should not disobey her father's kindly given instructions and, taking three melons, cut them lengthwise. At that instant, every one of the melons in the whole mountainlike pile split lengthwise, and from their midst issued a great flood that swept Mikeran away.

The river that came from the melons can still be seen in the autumn sky. It is the Milky Way. Mikeran became the star Altair, and the woman became the star Vega. They are separated by the Milky Way and are said to cry continuously. The seven-year-old and five-year-old children became the two stars close to the star Vega. Since the day this happened was on the seventh day of the seventh month, it is only on that day that Mikeran and the woman from heaven can meet.

The child which the woman dropped as she was ascending to heaven fell safely to earth, where each year its mother would send three *koku* [about 1,500 pounds] of rice, leaving them on the bank of a mountain stream. The child was able to live for a whole year on this rice. However, one day a woman came and washed some dirty things in the river, and the three *koku* shrank to only three grains of rice. People say that the child disappeared without ever being seen again.

The Fire Boy

Types 314 III, V, VI, The Youth Transformed to a Horse, and 313 IV, The Girl as Helper in the Hero's Flight, as well as the male Cinderella theme, Motif L101, "Unpromising hero," figure in this tale. Kata No. 216, "The Fire Boy." Collected on Okierabu Island, Oshima-gun, Kagoshima-ken, from Kubomori Sashi.

This tale is not widespread throughout Japan, and only seven variants are on record, so it may have been recently introduced. The elements of the tale have, however, been so completely adapted to Japanese tradition that it is difficult without further study to state if or when it was borrowed. Only the obstacle-flight motif (see note to No. 19), which occurs in both Types 313 and 314, has been thoroughly studied.

In Japan's feudal period, government officials in outlying districts were required to make periodic trips to Edo, the seat of the shogunate. In Japanese tales, this period of enforced absence is often used by an evil stepmother to persecute or drive away her husband's children. Cf. No. 30.

The anniversary of the death of a close relative is observed with offerings of incense and flowers. Places of entertainment are avoided on that day.

• LONG AGO a son was born to the lord of the country of Omura. The son was named Mamichigane. When Mamichigane was three years old, his mother died and his father married again; so Mamichigane was raised by a stepmother.

When Mamichigane was nine years old, his father, the lord, had to go up to Edo for three months. When he got ready to go, he said to his wife, "You will have nothing to do but comb and care for Mamichigane's hair; please do it every day." And he set off on his journey.

The mother went to the lord's ship to see him off, then she returned. From that time she began to treat Mamichigane very cruelly. "Today you must go to the mountains and bring home some firewood," she said. When he had brought the wood, she commanded, "Now rake the garden." And she kept him working all the time. Instead of caring for his hair, she let it get dirty and lousy. In a short while Mamichigane became a dirty, unkempt child.

Finally the three months passed. A letter came saying that the father's ship would return the next day. The mother said to Mamichigane, "Tomorrow your father will be returning, so you must work very hard to gather the wood and rake the garden."

The next day Mamichigane said, "Mother, let us go to meet father's ship." "You go first," she said; "I will arrange my hair and come later." And so she sent Mamichigane on ahead. Then she took a razor and cut her face with it, covered herself with the bed covers, and went to sleep. Mamichigane went to meet the ship, and when his father saw his dirty appearance, he asked, "How have you come to look like this?"

"Because mother didn't take care of me," he replied.

"What is wrong with your mother?"

"She said that she would dress her hair and then come," he said, and so the two of them waited for her. However, they grew tired of waiting, and both of them, father and son, went home. When they got there they saw that the mother was sleeping. When the father asked why, she pushed back the covers, lifted her head, and said: "Look at what your child has done to me. As soon as your ship was gone, he would come every day with a razor, and crying, 'You old stepmother, you,' he would cut gashes in my face. I was ashamed to be seen looking like this; so I could not come to meet your ship."

When the father heard this, he refused to listen to anything the boy said and cried, "Such an undutiful son as you deserves to be banished!" He chose the best one of three horses and gave it to him, along with the kimonos that he had brought as presents from Edo; then he sent him out of the house.

Mamichigane, wearing the beautiful kimonos and riding the horse, set off for the south, leaving the village behind. He continued riding and riding until he came to a river one thousand *ri* [about 2,440 miles] long and one *ri* [about 2½ miles] wide. He could not go around either end of the river. He said, "Watch how my horse jumps the river!" He hit the horse with the whip once, and in a flash he was across the river. He continued riding on and on and came to a cloud-shrouded thorn mountain. He could go neither right nor left. He cried, "This will not be hard. Watch how my horse jumps this," and he hit him once with the whip. The horse lowered his head. He hit him again, and in a flash they had jumped over the mountain.

He rode on and on and came to where an old man with long scraggly hair was cutting millet grass. "Grandfather, grandfather, is there anyone in this village who is looking for someone to work for him?" he asked.

"At the house of the *choja* who lives on the mountain to the west, one of the thirty-five employees died, and today is the seventh day since then. They should be looking for someone to hire. But I don't think they would hire someone dressed as you are."

"Then let me exchange my kimono for your working clothes."

"I am afraid that I would be punished if I exchanged my clothes for such a beautiful kimono as you are wearing. I will just give my working clothes to you."

"It is my wish, grandfather, so let us please exchange. Please lend me a trunk, and I'll put the kimono I am wearing in it and leave it with you."

The old man agreed to this, and so the boy put on the old man's working clothes and put his own kimono and the horse's saddle in the trunk. He turned the horse loose on a nearby bamboo covered mountain which was one *ri* around. Then together with the old man, he went to the house of the *choja* on the mountain to the west. He asked if he could get employment there. It was soon agreed that he should be hired, and so he went to work there.

The boy, having been employed by the rich man, was sent to cut fodder. He soon found it too difficult and returned to the master. "I keep cutting my hands, I cannot cut grass. Please allow me to rake the garden," he requested. He was sent to rake the garden but soon said, "I do nothing but get blisters on my hands; I cannot rake the garden. Please let me do the cooking instead of the seven men now doing it."

"All right, all right, you may do whatever you wish," replied the master. The boy said, "Please let me use the seven cooks for one day."

He had one man bring dirt, one bring stones, two carry water, one cut straw, and two mix mortar. In a short while he had built seven stone stoves. After that the rice for the three daily meals could be cooked very rapidly. Until that time, breakfast had been at noon, lunch had been in the evening, and supper at midnight; but now just as soon as dawn broke, he could call, "Please come to breakfast," and on the stroke of noon, "Please come to lunch," and as the sun was setting, "Please come to supper."

The master was very happy and said, "I have found that you are a very good fire boy; I'd like to have you work here all the time. Tomorrow there is going to be a dancing performance, so I want you to make lunch earlier than usual." The next morning when the fire boy was preparing the meal, the master came to him and said, "I'd like you to come along to the dancing too."

"I am sorry but today is the third anniversary of my mother's death; I cannot go to a place of entertainment today."

"Then please stay here and take care of things; we will go to see the dancing," said the master.

"Yes sir," said the fire boy. He waited until the master and everyone else had left; then he took a bath and put on the most beautiful of the robes which he had left at the old man's house. He put on splendid high wooden clogs and called his horse from the bamboo grove. He saddled it, then rode and stood at the north edge of the dancing stage. "Watch Mamichigane's horse dance!" he called out. He hit it once with the whip. The horse jumped over the stage and landed on the south side of it.

The lord of the province and all the spectators cried out, "A deity has come down from heaven, let us stand and worship him," and they all worshiped the boy.

The rich man from the west mountain also worshiped, but his daughter, who was just coming of age, said, "That is our fire boy; there is a black mark on his left ear."

"Do not profane the deities. Hurry, worship him!" said her father, so the girl laughingly began to worship.

The fire boy returned home before anyone else, turned the

horse loose on the bamboo mountain, put away his clothes at the old man's place, put his working clothes back on, and using the bamboo fire bellows as a pillow, went to sleep.

After a while the rich man came home and called, "Fire boy, fire boy, open the front gate." When the fire boy had opened the gate, the master said, "You really should have gone today; a deity came down from heaven to the dancing place, and everyone worshiped him."

"Oh, did that really happen? It would have been nice to have been there," said the fire boy.

"Day after tomorrow there will be dancing again; so please get up early and fix our meals," requested the master.

When that day came, the fire boy got up early and fixed breakfast for everyone. The master said, "Please come along with us," but the fire boy replied, "Today is the anniversary of my grandfather's death."

After everyone had left, the fire boy took a bath, got ready, and saddled his horse. Just then the daughter returned home on the pretext that she had forgotten her sandals. Since there was nothing else he could do, the fire boy took her on his horse and together they went and stood on the east side of the dancing stage. "Mamichigane's horse will dance; everyone watch!" he called out and hit the horse once with the whip. The horse jumped and landed by the stage house on the west side of the stage. When the lord and the rich man saw this they cried, "To-day the deities have come as man and wife!" and everyone worshiped.

The fire boy and the girl returned home ahead of everyone else. The fire boy turned the horse out on the bamboo mountain, changed his clothes and, taking the bamboo fire bellows as a pillow, lay down to sleep. The girl said that her stomach hurt and shut herself in one of the rooms at the rear of the house.

Soon the master came home. "Fire boy, open the front gate," he called. "You really should have gone today for sure; today the deity came with his wife," he said.

"Yes, I really should have gone," said the fire boy.

When the master entered the house and found that his daughter had a stomach-ache, he made a great to-do. He was going to call a doctor, but the girl said, "I do not need a doctor; please call a shrine priestess."

Three priestesses were called, and after they had made a divination, they said, "This illness is not caused by anything in particular; it is just a chronic weakness."

The girl, however, did not agree. "Please call that priestess who has just recently come to the shrine," she requested. So the new priestess was called; she made a divination and said, "This is not a chronic disease. There is someone among the seventeen men who serve here whom she likes. If you have each of the seventeen men dress in the way they wish, the one to whom the girl offers a cup will be the one whom she likes."

The rich man had all seventeen of his male employees do as the priestess had said, but the girl offered the cup to none of them. "Isn't there anyone else?" asked the rich man and was told that there remained only the dirty, filthy fire boy.

"The fire boy is a man just like any of you. Have him get ready, and bring him here," and the rich man loaned him his own old clothes to wear.

The fire boy took a bath and used the clothes loaned him by the rich man to dry with; then he took them and threw them in the pig pen. Next he was loaned better clothes; these he also wiped himself dry with, then threw them behind the stables. Next he was loaned a very beautiful robe; this too he used to dry on, then threw it in the toilet. Finally he put on the clothes he had left at the old man's house, mounted his horse, and came to the master. When the rich man saw him he took him by the hand and led him to where his daughter was. Her disease was immediately healed. She took the cup and offered it to the fire boy.

The rich man said, "I wasn't able to understand as well as my daughter. Please, will you become my son-in-law?"

And so the wedding ceremony began. Three days of celebration passed, and on the fourth day the bridegroom said to the rich man, "Please may I have three days, I would like to go and see my parents."

"No," said the rich man, "I will not give you three days; you may have today, just this one day," and so the young man was given one day free and made ready to go. His wife asked, "Will you be taking the road along the sea, or will you take the mountain road?"

"If I go by the road along the sea, it will take three days, but if I go over the mountains, it will take only one day; so I will take the mountain road," he said.

"While you are going along the mountain road, some mulberry fruit will fall into your saddle, but no matter how thirsty you are, you must not eat it. If you eat the mulberries, we can never meet one another again," said the wife.

As the young man was riding along the mountain road, some mulberries fell into the horse's saddle. Since his wife had warned him so strictly not to eat them, he did not do so at first; but finally his throat became so dry that he could bear it no longer, and he ate one of them. When he did that he immediately died and fell over onto the horse's neck. The horse went along carrying the dead Mamichigane. When the horse came to an uphill slope he would bend his front legs, and on a downhill slope he would bend his rear legs, so that the body did not fall off. Finally he came to the house where Mamichigane was born. He stood at the gate and whinnied three times.

The father heard it and said: "That is Mamichigane's horse, but it is strange that no one calls for me, only the horse whinnies. Please go and see what is wrong," and his wife went to look.

When the mother opened the gate, the horse attacked her and killed her. The father went to see what was the matter. He took Mamichigane from the horse and put him in a wine cask, then put on the lid, saying, "Instead of coming back alive, you have come back dead. Why?"

Mamichigane's wife said to herself: "If I knew where his home was, I could write a letter. He was to have returned in one day, but three days have passed and he hasn't returned." She was sure that he must have eaten some of the mulberries. She bought three *go* [about three cups] of life-restoring water and set out, not even knowing where he lived. She walked in only half a day the road which had taken Mamichigane's horse a full day and soon arrived at Mamichigane's house.

"Is this Mamichigane's house," she asked.

His father came out. "Yes, it is," he replied.

"Please show me his body."

"I cannot show my own son's body to a total stranger."

"I am not a stranger. He was my husband, and on the fourth day after our marriage, he set out for here. Please show him to me."

"Then I have wronged you. Please take a look at him," and the father took his body from the wine cask and showed it to her. He looked as though he were not really dead but only asleep.

The wife took some water and washed his body, then rubbed him with the life-restoring water. When she did this Mamichigane returned to life saying, "I was sleeping in the morning, I was sleeping in the evening."

"You weren't sleeping in the morning. You weren't sleeping in the evening. You ate the mulberries that I told you not to eat and you died. I have revived you with this life-restoring water. Come, let us return home."

"This is my only son; I cannot let him go," said the father.

"Then I will stay here," said the wife.

"I cannot take care of two fathers," said Mamichigane; "I will send you money, and you can adopt another son. I will go to my wife's house, since she has saved my life," and so the two of them bade the father goodby and returned home.

It is said that they are still living happily, even to this day.

•25• *The Crane Wife*

Motif B652.2, "*Man marries crane in human form*," *is the primary motif of this tale. Kata No. 146,* "*The Crane Wife.*" *Collected in Satsuma-gun, Kagoshima-ken.*

This tale is one of the best known of many Japanese stories dealing with non-human or enchanted brides. It has been made into a popular drama by Junji Kinoshita, pp. 107–41. Dorson, in Folk Legends of Japan, *pp. 81–83, gives a legend of a grateful pheasant who appeared as a young woman to reward her bene-factor.*

The German folklorist, Josef Kohler, examined the Melusina myth, the story of an enchanted wife lost through the disobedi-ence of her mortal husband, but he had no versions of the Crane Wife available when he made his study in 1895.

The crane is even better known in Japan than in Western coun-tries as a symbol of good luck and long life. The folding of paper cranes and stringing them into long chains is a favorite chidren's pastime to which a religious significance is often at-tached. Millions of paper cranes were used by Japanese people in a recent plea for the outlawing of nuclear weapons.

• ONCE THERE was a man named Karoku. He lived with his seventy-year-old mother far back in the mountains, where he made charcoal for a living. One winter, as he was going to the village to buy some *futon* [bedding], he saw a crane struggling in a trap where it had been caught.

Just as Karoku was stooping to release the poor crane, the man who had set the trap came running up. "What are you doing, in-terfering with other people's business?" he cried.

"I felt so sorry for the crane I thought I would let it go. Will you sell it to me? Here, I have the money I was going to use to buy *futon*. Please take the money, and let me have the crane." The man agreed, and Karoku took the crane and immediately let it fly away free.

"Well," thought Karoku, returning home, "we may get cold tonight, but it can't be helped." When he got home, his mother asked what he had done with the *futon*. He replied, "I saw a crane caught in a trap. I felt so sorry for it that I used all the money to buy it and set it free."

"Well," his mother said, "since you have done it, I suppose that it is all right."

The next evening, just as night was falling, a beautiful young lady such as they had never seen before came to Karoku's house. "Please let me spend the night here," she asked, but Karoku refused, saying, "My little hut is too poor." She replied, "No, I do not mind; please, I implore you, let me stay," until finally he consented, and she was allowed to spend the night.

During the evening she said, "I have something I should like to discuss with you," and when Karoku asked what it was, she replied, "I beg of you, please make me your wife."

Karoku, greatly surprised, said: "This is the first time in my life that I have seen such a beautiful woman as you. I am a very poor man; I do not even know where my next meal is coming from; how could I ever take you as my wife?"

"Please do not refuse," she pleaded; "please take me as your wife."

"Well, you beg me so much, I don't know what to do,'" he replied. When his mother heard this, she said to her, "Since you insist, you may become my son's bride. Please stay here and work hard." Soon preparations were made, and they were married.

Some time after this his wife said, "Please put me in a cabinet and leave me there for three days. Close the door tightly and be sure not to open it and look at me." Her husband put her in a cabinet, and on the fourth day, she came out. "It must have been very unpleasant in there," he said. "I was worried about you. Hurry and have something to eat."

"All right," she said. After she finished eating she said, "Karoku, Karoku, please take the cloth that I wove while in the cabinet and sell it for two thousand *ryo*." Saying this, she took a bolt of cloth from the cabinet and gave it to her husband. He took it to the lord of the province, who, when he saw it, said, "This is very beautiful material, I will pay you two or even three thousand *ryo* for it. Can you bring me another bolt like it?"

"I must ask my wife if she can weave another," Karoku replied.

"Oh, you need not ask her; it is all right if only you agree. I will give you the money for it now," the lord said.

Karoku returned home and told his wife what the lord had said. "Just give me time and I'll weave another bolt," she said. "This time please shut me in the cabinet for one week. During that time you must be sure not to open the door and look at me." And so he shut her in the cabinet again.

By the time the week was nearly over, Karoku became very worried about his wife. On the last day of the week, he opened the door to see if she were all right. There inside the cabinet was a crane, naked after having pulled out all her beautiful long feathers. She was using her feathers to weave the cloth and was just at the point of finishing it.

The crane cried out, "I have finished the cloth, but since you have seen who I really am, I am afraid that you can no longer love me. I must return to my home. I am not a person but the crane whom you rescued. Please take the cloth to the lord as you promised."

After she had said this, the crane silently turned toward the west. When she did this, thousands of cranes appeared, and taking her with them, they all flew out of sight.

Karoku had become a rich man, but he wanted to see his beloved wife so badly that he could not bear it. He searched for her throughout Japan until he was exhausted. One day as he was sitting on the seashore resting, he saw an old man alone in a rowboat, approaching from the open ocean. "How strange," thought Karoku. "Where could he be coming from; there are no islands near here." As he sat in bewilderment, the boat landed on the beach. Karoku called out, "Grandfather, where did you come from?"

"I came from an island called 'The Robe of Crane Feathers,'" the old man replied.

"Would you please take me to that island?" asked Karoku.

The old man quickly agreed, and Karoku climbed into the boat. The boat sped over the water, and in no time they had arrived at a beautiful white beach. They landed, and when Karoku got out of the boat and turned around, the boat and the old man had vanished from sight.

Karoku walked up the beach and soon came to a beautiful pond. In the middle of the pond was an island, and there on the island was the naked crane. She was surrounded by a myriad of cranes, for she was queen of the cranes.

Karoku stayed a short while and was given a feast. Afterward the old man with the boat returned, and Karoku was taken back to his home.

·26· The Snow Wife

Motif T11.0.1, "Marriage to supernatural wives who disappear,"
is applicable here. Kata No. 366, "The Snow Wife." Collected
in Fujisaki-mura, Minami Tsugaru-gun, Aomori-ken, from the
grandmother of collector Yutaro Kawai.

The tale of the snow wife is widely distributed throughout
the northwestern part of Japan, particularly on the west coast.
There the snow often reaches a depth of ten feet or more and
remains on the ground up to six months of the year. The text
given here is shorter than most. In many versions of the tale
there is a prior meeting of the man and the snow woman; the
man is enjoined never to mention this fact. When he does mention it some time later, the snow woman disappears. Lafcadio
Hearn has a well-developed version of this tale in his Kwaidan,
pp. 111–18.

The snow woman is generally pictured as though her only visible parts are long hair, facial features, and pubic hair. The remainder of her body blends with the whiteness of the snow
until the time she takes on complete human form to live with
mortals.

• LONG AGO there was a young man who was a bachelor. One
winter night during a heavy snowstorm he thought that he
heard someone outside and opened the door to see. When he
opened the door, he saw that a young woman had fallen in a
heap by the door. He had never seen her before. "Hallo, hallo!
What's the matter!" he cried and helped the woman into the
house. She was a beautiful young woman, and he took her as
his bride.

Soon she became well and strong, and they lived happily together; but as spring approached and the weather became
warmer, she gradually became thinner and thinner and her
health began to fail.

One day the man's friends came for a party. As they were

drinking *sake* and eating, the man called to his wife, but she did
not answer. Wondering what was the matter, he went to the
kitchen and saw that in front of the kitchen stove there was
nothing but his wife's kimono lying in a pool of water.

•27• *The Snail* Choja

*Type 425, The Search for the Lost Husband, episodes Ia, c, IId.
Kata No. 151, "The Mud-Snail Son." Collected in Tono-mura,
Kamihei-gun, Iwate-ken, from Kinzo Ogasawara.*

*Stories about enchanted bridegrooms are extremely popular
in Europe as well as in Japan. Thompson, p. 99, notes that
several countries in western Europe have each reported more
than fifty versions of the best-known enchanted bridegroom
tale of all, that of Cupid and Psyche. The oldest recorded variant
is found in* The Golden Ass *by Apuleius, written in the second
century after Christ.*

*Japanese tradition includes many different tales in which ani-
mal or enchanted bridegrooms are featured. The tale of the
snail husband is widely distributed throughout Japan, with thirty-
five versions recorded. See No. 28, "Little One Inch," for the
story of another miniature hero.*

*In Japan, where to be childless is considered extremely unfor-
tunate, a couple's desire for a child of any kind, even a snail
child, would be accepted as natural by the hearers of the tale.*

*Brides returned to visit their parents a month or more after
marriage. At that time they also reported their marriage to the
graves of their ancestors. This visit completed the marriage for-
malities.*

• LONG, LONG ago, there lived in a certain place a *choja* [rich
man]. The people in the village said that he was so rich that he
could not possibly be in need of anything.

Among the farmers who cultivated the rich man's estate,
there were one man and his wife who were so poor that they
sometimes had nothing at all to eat. They were already over forty

years old, but for some reason or other they had no children. Every night before they went to bed, they would lament the fact that they were childless, saying to one another, "Oh, how much we would like to have a child; how nice it would be to have something to call our own child, even if it were only a frog or a snail." They often went to the shrine of the water deity and prayed that they might have a child.

One day, going out as usual to cut the grass growing along the edge of the rice fields, the farmer's wife prayed with all her heart to the water deity. "Honorable Water Deity, please give me a child, even if it is only like one of the snails here in the rice fields. I beg of you, hear my prayer."

As she said this, for some reason her stomach began to hurt. She tried her best to bear the pain, but it gradually became worse and worse, until finally she could no longer endure it and had to crawl home on her hands and knees. Her husband, greatly worried, tried to ease the pain, but no matter what he did, it did not get any better. There was no money with which to pay the doctor even if they were to call one; they were completely at a loss as to what to do. Fortunately a midwife lived in the neighborhood, and although she was not a doctor, they decided to call her. They did so and found that the farmer's wife was going to give birth to a baby. Upon hearing this, they were overjoyed and immediately lighted a candle before the *kamidana* [household shrine] and prayed that the water deity would help the baby to be born safely.

Shortly after this the wife gave birth to a tiny baby snail. Everyone was very much surprised, but since it was sent from the water deity, they determined to take very good care of it. They put it in a bowl of water and set it in front of the *kamidana*.

Twenty years passed. Strangely enough the Snail Boy grew no larger. He never spoke a word; however, he ate as much as anyone. One day, as the old farmer was loading the horses with the *nengumai* [yearly rice tax] which had to be paid each year to the *choja* who owned the land, he sighed to himself: "Ahh, ahh, it was generous of the water deity to give us a child, and we are very thankful, but it is a snail child. Since he is only a snail, he cannot help me at all, and I have had to work all my life, taking care of my wife and this child."

Just as he was lamenting his fate, he heard a voice coming from somewhere: "Father, father, I'll deliver the rice for you." The old man looked around but saw no one. "This is strange," he thought. "Who could that be?"

"It is I, father. For a long time you have taken good care of me, and it is now time for me to go out into the world. Today I will take the rice to the master for you."

"But how will you drive the horses?"

"Since I am only a snail, I can't actually drive the horses, but if you put me up on one of the bales of rice, the horses can go along by themselves with no trouble at all, and I'll just ride along."

The old man was greatly surprised to hear that the Snail Boy, who until then had never spoken a word, could not only talk but even wanted to go and deliver the rice to the landowner. However, since the Snail Boy had been sent by the water deity, the old man was afraid that he might be punished if he refused to do as requested. He loaded up the rice on the three horses, then took the Snail Boy from the bowl in front of the *kamidana* and put him up on top of one of the rice bales.

"Well, father and mother, I'll go and be back soon," said the Snail Boy, as he started off. *"Haido, haido shishi"* [get up, get up]; calling out to the horses like an expert driver, he drove out the gate and down the road.

The old man had let the boy take the horses, but he could not help worrying about whether everything would be all right; so he secretly followed along behind. However, the Snail Boy drove the horses like a real horseman; when he came to a ford or a bridge, he would call out, *"haai, hai, shan shan"* [whoa, easy now], in a loud voice, just like a real driver. And not only this, he sang the songs that drivers sing in a loud clear voice, so that the horses fell into step with the song, the bells on their necks going *janka, gonka,* jingle, jangle, in tune with the song, and so they went merrily on their way.

The people walking along the road and the people working

in the rice fields heard a voice but saw no one driving the horses. They thought it very, very strange. "Those skinny horses certainly belong to that poor farmer, but who is singing the driver's songs?" they wondered, looking on in astonishment.

The boy's father, seeing everything that took place, wondered how it had all come about. He hurried back home and knelt down in front of the *kamidana* with his wife. They prayed: "Oh, honorable Water Deity, hear our prayer. We have been so ignorant. You have given us such a wonderful son, and we have treated him so miserably. We beg you to protect him and guide him and the horses safely to the *choja*'s house."

The Snail Boy drove along without any trouble and came to the *choja*'s house. The servants, hearing that someone had come to deliver the yearly rice tax, went out to the front gate, but they saw only the horses; no one was with them. "What is this," they said; "the horses couldn't have come by themselves." But as they were talking they heard a voice from the midst of the rice bales, "I've brought the yearly rice tax; please let me down."

"What! Who's up there? We don't see anybody," they called out. They searched through the rice bales and found the tiny Snail Boy.

"I'm sorry to trouble you," the Snail Boy said, "but since I'm so small, I'm not able to unload the rice myself; won't you please do it for me? Be careful not to crush me. Just put me over there on the edge of the verandah, and I'll be quite safe."

The servants were very astonished to see the snail and hear it talking and immediately called the *choja*. "Master, master, a snail has come bringing the yearly rice tax."

The master of the house went out to see, and sure enough, there was the snail with the rice, just as the servants had said. Soon everyone in the whole house came out to see, exclaiming that this was the strangest thing they had ever seen.

Soon the rice was all unloaded as the snail had directed and was piled up in the storehouse; then the horses were given some hay. The Snail Boy was invited into the house for dinner. He perched up on the edge of the tray, and although no one could tell just how it happened, the rice in the bowl gradually became less and less. Next the soup began to diminish, and then the fish slowly disappeared.

At last the Snail Boy finished. He thanked his hosts for the delicious meal and asked if he might be served tea.

The *choja* had heard that the child which had been sent by the water deity to one of the farmers on his estate was a snail, but he did not know that the Snail Boy was able to talk and work just like a real person. The *choja* decided that in some way or other he would keep him as his own.

Thinking that he might be able to keep the Snail Boy without paying anything for him, the *choja* made a proposition, saying, "You know, Snail Boy, ever since your grandfather's time, your family and my family have had friendly relations with one another. Now, I have two daughters, and if you like, you may have one of them as your wife."

The Snail Boy, hearing this, was overjoyed and asked if it were really true.

"Quite true," said the *choja*. "I promise that I will give you one of my daughters as your wife."

So the Snail Boy, having been well entertained, returned home. His father and mother were beginning to get very worried, since it was becoming late and he had not come home; they feared that something had happened to him on the way. But just then he returned in high spirits, bringing the three horses with him.

During supper he told how he had been offered one of the *choja*'s daughters as his wife. His father and mother could hardly believe that it was true, but since the Snail Boy had been given to them by the water deity, they felt that it must be so. Just to make sure, they decided to ask the boy's aunt to go and see if the *choja* really meant what he had said.

When the aunt arrived at the *choja*'s house, he called his two daughters and said, "Which one of you would like to go to be the bride of the Snail Boy?"

The older sister cried out in disgust: "What! Get married to a filthy snail! It makes me sick to think of it!" She stamped her foot angrily and flounced out of the room.

The younger sister, however, was very gentle and kind. "Since you have promised that one of us should go to be the snail's bride, I will go. Please do not worry any more," she said reassuringly.

The aunt, hearing this answer from the *choja,* returned to the old man and his wife and told them all that had happened.

When it came time for the *choja*'s younger daughter to go to the Snail Boy's house for the wedding, the dowry was so large that not even seven horses could carry it. There were seven chests of drawers and seven trunks of kimonos; there were more pieces of hand baggage than one could count. Since they could not get it all into the poor farmer's house, the *choja* built a special storehouse to put it in. The bridegroom could furnish nothing, and since there were no relatives except the one aunt, the only guests at the wedding were the old father and mother, the aunt, and an old woman who lived close by.

The old man and his wife were very happy to have such a beautiful daughter-in-law. She was a great help to them, going out in the fields and working very hard all day, and so their lives became more comfortable and pleasant than they had ever known before. Feeling that all this had been given them by the water deity, they came to believe in him more and more devoutly.

After some time had passed, the day for the daughter-in-law to return to visit her parents drew near. It was decided that she should go soon after the festival which was always held on the eighth of April in honor of Yakushi-*sama* [Buddhist deity of healing], one of the patron deities of the village.

Spring came and the flowers began to bloom. Soon the eighth of April arrived and with it the festival of Yakushi-*sama*. The Snail Boy's bride decided that she would go and see the festival celebrations; so she carefully powdered her face, chose a beautiful kimono from one of the trunks, and put it on. She was so beautiful that she looked almost like a person from heaven. Having finished her dressing, she suggested to her snail husband, "Let's go together and enjoy the festival."

"Yes, let's do that," he agreed. "It's such nice weather today, and I haven't been out of doors for a long time." And so the beautiful bride put the snail in the fastener in the front of the sash of her kimono, and they set off together for the festival.

The girl walked along with the snail in her sash, the two of them talking and laughing together. The people they passed along the road shook their heads saying, "Ah, it's a pity, such a beautiful girl talking and laughing to herself; too bad that she has lost her mind."

The two of them went on until they came to the outer entrance of Yakushi-*sama's* shrine. Then the snail said to his wife: "I'm sorry, but for some reason, I can't go into the shrine with you. Just put me down here along the edge of the road by one of the rice paddy paths; you go by yourself and worship at the shrine. I'll wait for you here."

"Oh, really? Well, do be careful and don't let a bird or something eat you up. Wait just a moment, and I'll go up and say a prayer and be back very quickly." Saying this, she went up the hill to the main temple, where she prayed. She then hurried back to where she had left her husband, but he was not there. Greatly surprised, she searched hither and thither, but he was nowhere to be found.

Thinking that perhaps a bird might have eaten him up or that he might have fallen into the middle of the rice fields, she waded out into the rice paddies and searched everywhere. Since it was April, there were many, many snails in the muddy fields, and she picked them up one by one; but although they were all snails, none of them looked like her husband.

> Snail, my snail,
> Oh, my husband.
> Ah, it is spring,
> An evil old crow
> Might have swooped down
> And eaten you.

Singing this song, she searched in the muddy water until her face was splattered and her beautiful kimono was completely covered with mud. It began to grow late, and people returning from the festival saw the girl wading in the mud. "Such a beautiful girl," they said; "how sad it is that she has lost her mind."

No matter how much she searched, she was unable to find her husband. Giving up in despair, she decided to throw herself down where the mud was deepest and drown. Just as she was about to fling herself face down in the mud, she heard a voice behind her saying, "Here, here, girl! What are you doing?"

She looked around, and there stood a handsome young man. He had a straw hat on his head and at his waist hung a flute. The girl told the young man all that had happened, then said, "Now, I am going to drown myself."

"You needn't worry any more," the young man said; "I am the snail that you were looking for."

The girl, thinking that what he said was impossible, refused to believe him.

"You should not doubt me," he said; "I am the child sent by the water deity. Up until now I have been disguised as a snail, but today, since you went to worship at the shrine of Yakushi-*sama,* I could first appear in human form. I went to worship at the water deity's shrine, and when I came back here you were gone. I have been searching everywhere for you."

Hearing this, the girl was filled with joy, and the two of them happily returned home together. While everyone had said that the girl was beautiful, the young man was no less handsome. When the young couple entered the house, the happiness of the young man's father and mother was beyond all description.

They immediately went to tell the *choja* what had happened. He came with his wife to see the snail son-in-law who had been changed into a real man. They were overjoyed upon seeing him, saying, "With such a handsome son, it is a shame that they should live in such a wretched hovel; let us build a mansion for them." So in the best part of the village they built a splendid big house, and the young man and his wife became merchants. The news that this was the young man who had been a snail was soon spread throughout the surrounding countryside, and his business prospered until it was not long before he was the richest man in the village.

The young man's aged father and mother were able to spend the rest of their lives in ease, and arrangements were made for the aunt to marry into a fine family. The young man became

known as the Snail *Choja,* and he and all his relatives became
very, very prosperous and wealthy.

•28•   Little One Inch

*Type 700, Tom Thumb. Kata No. 153, "Issun Boshi, 'Little One
Inch.'" Collected in Tokorozawa-mura, Iruma-gun, Saitama-ken,
from the maid of collector Mitsue Hitabayashi.*

*Thompson, p. 87, notes that the tale of Tom Thumb is very
popular as a nursery tale and has doubtless been propagated
largely through children's books and use in the nursery. This ob-
servation seems to be as true for Japan as for Europe; there is
even a well-known children's song which describes Little One
Inch's trip to Kyoto, the capital city. Numerous other tales are
told of miniature children, often in animal form; see e.g., No. 27,
"The Snail Choja."*

*A wish-fulfilling hammer is a favorite type of magical instru-
ment in Japanese tales.*

• ONCE LONG ago in a certain place there lived a man and his
wife who loved one another very much. They had no children,
but they wanted one so badly that they said that even a child
as small as the end of a finger would be all right. One day they
went to the shrine of Sumiyoshi-*sama* and prayed with all their
might, "Sumiyoshi-*sama,* please give us a child, even if it is only
as big as the end of a finger."

Now it happened that ten months after this, a charming little
baby boy was born. The baby, however, was so tiny that it was
only as large as the end of a finger, so they named him Issun
Boshi, 'Little One Inch.' They raised him with loving care, but
no matter how much time passed, he never grew any bigger at
all. One day they decided to give him a sewing needle as a
sword and send him away from home.

There was nothing else Little One Inch could do, so he took
the rice bowl and chopsticks his mother gave him and set off.

He used the rice bowl as a boat and the chopsticks as oars and started off for the capital city. After many, many days he finally arrived at the emperor's capitol. He walked about here and there, and after a while he stopped in front of a splendid big house. He went into the entrance hall of the house and called as loud as he could, "I beg indulgence, I beg indulgence!"

The people of the house thought it a strange-sounding voice and, wondering who it was, went to the entrance hall to see. There they saw the tiny little boy standing under the wooden clogs. "Little boy, was it you who called just now?"

"Yes it was; I am called Little One Inch. I have been sent away from home by my parents. Would you please take me into your house?" They thought him interesting, so they decided to take care of him. Little One Inch was small, but he was very clever. Whatever they asked him, he knew much more, and soon everyone was calling, "Little One Inch, Little One Inch," because they loved him so much. The daughter of the house, especially, came to be very fond of him.

One day she took Little One Inch with her and went to pray to the goddess Kannon. On the way back, two *oni* met them. They were just about to seize the girl when Little One Inch drew the needle from its scabbard at his waist and brandishing it about, cried as loud as he could, "I don't know who you think I am. Well, I am Little One Inch who has accompanied the master's daughter on a pilgrimage to Kannon-*sama!*" In spite of this, one of the *oni* took Little One Inch and swallowed him whole. Since Little One Inch was so small, he could move about easily in the *oni's* stomach. Waving his sword about, he danced around puncturing the *oni's* stomach. The *oni* was so surprised that he coughed Little One Inch up and spit him out. When he did that the other *oni* grabbed him and was going to crush him, but Little One Inch saw his chance and jumped into the *oni's* eye. The *oni's* eye hurt so that both the *oni* ran away.

Little One Inch started home with the girl, who all this time had been standing to one side shaking with fright. Just as they set off, they saw a little hammer that had been dropped along the way. The girl picked it up, and Little One Inch asked what it was. The girl said, "This is a magic striking hammer. No matter what you want, you can strike with the hammer and you will get it."

"Then please strike me with it and see if you can make me grow taller, will you," asked Little One Inch. The girl waved the hammer and cried, "Grow taller, grow taller," and to their surprise Little One Inch's body began to grow and grow until soon he became a splendid young samurai.

•29• *The White Bird Sister*

Type 403A, The Black and the White Bride. Kata No. 220, "The White Bird Sister." Collected in Okierabu Island, Oshima-gun, Kagoshima-ken, from Kubomori Sashi.

Thompson, p. 118, notes that several hundred versions of the tale of the substituted bride are found in Europe; in addition it is known in Africa and India and has been carried to widely scattered tribes of North American Indians. The tale forms the frame in which the fifty tales of Basile's seventeenth-century Pentamerone are told. In Japan the tale is not widespread, although four well told versions have been collected in southern districts.

According to Japanese Buddhist belief, the soul of the deceased does not begin its journey to the other world until the seventh day after death. In folktales the soul often appears during this period to the deceased's survivors in bird or animal form. In real life, observances are held on the seventh day, and the soul is thought to then begin its journey.

Putting the shining kimono under the dirty fireplace mats and placing the suribachi *grinding bowls on the gateposts are some of the unusual tasks often required of heroes in folktales. Conically shaped* suribachi *would not ordinarily sit upright on a gatepost.*

• LORD SASHU was ruler of the country called Sashu. He had a daughter and a son, but after they were born his wife died. The girl's name was Tama-no-Chu, and the boy's name was Kaniharu.

For ten years the lord waited patiently without taking another wife, but one day he said to his children: "Chu and Kaniharu, I think that I shall go and find a mother for you. Since you have no mother, I feel uncomfortable when other lords come to visit."

"Then please find one," the children said.

"I shall go and return in three days. Please take care of everything for me; your father will soon return with a mother for you," he said and made ready to leave.

For three days he walked about looking for a wife. He met many women, but he saw none that he wanted to take as his wife. When he came to a place called Yamada Muchi Nuyashi, he saw a beautiful woman weaving cloth. The lord called, "Excuse me, please," and the lady replied, "Oh, where have you come from? Here, please have some tobacco."

"I am Lord Sashu from the country of Sashu. My wife is dead, and I am hunting for another wife. Won't you please become my wife?"

"Yes. Please take me as your wife. My husband was the lord of Yamada Muchi, but when our only daughter was born he died, and I had to give up the manor. Now I live here and eke out a living by weaving. If you would take me and my daughter with you, it would be more than I had ever hoped for." And so it was decided, and the three of them returned to the lord's home.

"Tama-no-Chu, I have brought a new mother for you; come and greet her," the lord called. When Tama-no-Chu heard her father's voice she came out. "Your hair is just like my own mother's hair was. Your clothes are just like my own mother's clothes were. Please become our mother," said Tama-no-Chu. And so the woman became their new mother and took very good care of them.

Some time after this it was decided that Tama-no-Chu should become the bride of the lord Saga. The next day was set as the day on which she should go to be married. Her mother called her and said, "Tama-no-Chu, today you must go to Cedar Mountain and bring home some hemp. You must take the hemp and weave a steam-kettle strainer so that we can make malt." Tama-no-Chu went and got some hemp. Her mother put a large kettle of hot water on to boil and over the top of it spread the mat made from hemp.

"Now, Tama-no-Chu, you must take a bath on top of that," said her mother.

"Oh no, mother. I would fall into the boiling water and be scalded to death."

"Do you mean to say that a girl who is going to become the bride of such a handsome man as Lord Saga refuses to take a bath like this?" and grabbing Tama-no-Chu, she threw her into the boiling water.

Tama-no-Chu was scalded to death. When her brother Kaniharu saw this he began to cry so hard he nearly choked to death. The mother said to her husband, "Your former wife must have been a very bad person. Her daughter tried to take a bath in the hot water I had prepared in order to make malt for *miso,* and she fell in and was scalded to death."

When the father heard that he cried: "Oh, what a terrible thing! She was already betrothed; now what shall I tell the lord of Saga when he comes for her tomorrow."

"Please don't worry about it; Kana is here; we can get her ready and have her become the bride instead of Tama-no-Chu," said his wife, but the father felt a heavy pain in his chest and had to take to his bed.

The next day came. Couriers from the lord of Saga arrived to escort the bride to the lord's place. The father was sick, and so he could not go. Only the mother, Kana, and Kaniharu went.

When they arrived, they were given a great feast. When the time came to leave, the mother said to the lord, "Kaniharu is Tama-no-Chu's servant, so make sure he brings in wood every day and at night massages your and Chu's legs and shoulders."

The mother then returned home. "I changed Kana's name to Chu and gave her to the lord of Saga," she said.

"Where is Kaniharu?" asked the father.

"I thought that his sister would be lonely in a strange place, so I let him stay there for seven days and then come home," she said.

The next day Kana-no-Chu said, "Kaniharu, hurry and eat

breakfast, then go and gather firewood," and she sent him to the mountains to get firewood. Kaniharu knew neither which mountain to go to nor how to gather firewood. He could do nothing but go to the Cedar Mountain where the body of his elder sister was buried. He called out, "Cedar Mountain person, Cedar Mountain person," and from the grave where his sister was buried, a white bird came flying to him. It broke off the dead branches of the cedar trees, bundled them up, and gave them to the boy. Then it said, "I am your elder sister. What are you doing here?"

"I have been made to work hard gathering firewood, building fires, and even bathing and massaging people's legs."

"Really? Oh, I feel sorry for you. What is that you have on? Is that all you have to wear?"

"Yes, just this one shirt."

"Then go home and look by the storm doors of the weaving room. There should be some scraps of thread and weaving scraps thrown out there; pick some up and bring them to me; I will make you a new kimono from them."

Kaniharu left his sister, the white bird, and returned home. The next morning he got up early and went out to the weaving house. There he found pieces of thread and scraps of cloth. These he picked up and took to Cedar Mountain. "Cedar Mountain person!" he called, and the white bird came out.

"Did you find some pieces of thread and scraps of cloth?" she asked.

"I found some and brought them," he replied.

"Today you must gather firewood; then, when you take it home, say that your head hurts and go to bed. Do not eat supper, and for breakfast the next morning eat one bowlful of gruel. If there is gruel for lunch, eat one bowlful, but if there is rice, eat only half a bowlful; then stay in bed for three days. On the fourth morning, get up and say that you are completely well, then eat a good breakfast and come here to the mountain," said the white bird. Then she threw down some cedar branches and bundled them up for him.

Kaniharu put the firewood on his head and returned. He did as his elder sister, the white bird, had told him. He said that his head hurt; then he went to bed. On the morning of the fourth day he said, "I am well now. Today I shall go to the mountains and gather firewood," and so he set off for the mountains.

Arriving there he called, "Cedar Mountain person," and the white bird came carrying a kimono wrapped in a *furoshiki* [carrying cloth]. "I shall give you this kimono," she said. "Take it home with you, but never put it in a nice place. Put it under the dirtiest mat there is, under one in front of the stove. When you are sleeping at night and happen to wake up and feel cold, you can take out this kimono and wear it, but before morning comes you must take it off and put it back where it was. Now I shall get some firewood for you." She gathered up some firewood and gave it to him; then she said, "Today is the last day that I can be here. Tomorrow is the seventh day, and I must go and present myself to the king of the afterlife. You must not try to call me any more." After she had said this, the sister and brother parted.

Weeping, the boy returned home. He took the kimono and hid it under the dirty mat in front of the stove. That night after he had gone to sleep, he woke up feeling cold, and so he took the kimono from under the mat and put it on.

Now it happened that that night Lord Saga could not sleep. He called his retainers to bring some fire to light his pipe, but no one woke up. He called his wife, but she too did not awaken. There was nothing else to do, so he himself got up and went to the stove. There he saw something gleaming brightly. He thought it was something on fire and took the fire tongs to pick it up. He picked it up and saw that it was something big. He looked at it closely and found it to be a beautiful kimono. "What is this? Boy, where did you get this beautiful kimono?" he asked.

The boy began crying as if his heart would break, but the lord said, "I am not going to scold you or beat you; just tell me honestly all about it."

From the folds of his kimono, the boy took the keepsakes and mementos that had belonged to his older sister; then, pressing them into the lord's hand, he said, "Let us go outside, I will tell you everything." They went out, and as they walked along the road, the boy told everything that had happened up to that time.

"How is it that you did not tell me this earlier? Tomorrow morning get up early and make breakfast; we will go together to where your sister is."

"Tomorrow will be the seventh day since my sister died, and she will have already gone to the afterlife. She told me that she will not come back again."

"Regardless of that, we will have to go. I must make atonement to her. Hurry and make breakfast early, eat a lot, and make enough pressed rice balls for both of us." And so the two of them set out even before dawn.

They went to Cedar Mountain. The lord said, "If she sees me here, she may not come out; I will hide by the roots of this tree, and you can take some branches and cover me up," and so they hid him. Then Kaniharu called, "Cedar Mountain person!" and the white bird who was his elder sister came flying to him.

"What is the matter?" she asked. "Didn't I tell you very strictly not to call me any more? Here I was half way to the afterlife, and I have had to come back."

Just then the lord came out of his hiding place. "Can you become a human being again?" he asked.

"Up until yesterday I could have, but since today is the seventh day, I have already received my summons from the king of the afterlife and there is nothing I can do; but I will discuss this with him. In the meantime, go home and put two *suribachi* [grinding bowls] up on the gateposts, one on each post. Fill them with water and leave them there. Then if a white bird comes and bathes in the water, go and look on the little hill in the garden. At that time my body will be there. If you do not put the *suribachi* up on the gateposts, I can never become a human being again."

While the bird was talking, the lord tried to grab her, but she cried, "You must not touch me!"

"If I don't at least touch you, how can I go on living?" said the lord and tried to catch her again, but all he found in his hand were three flies.

The lord returned home. "Father, mother! The celebrations which we have just had were only empty celebrations. I beg of you, please put *suribachi* up on the gateposts."

"All the property here is yours. You can do anything you like with it," they said.

The lord took two *suribachi* and put them on the gateposts; they both stayed there very securely. Finally a white bird came flying down and bathed in one of the *suribachi*, then jumped out and bathed in the other. The lord went to the little hill in the garden; there behind the garden wash basin stood a radiantly beautiful girl, shining more brightly than the sun. The lord put her in a palanquin and lead her upstairs to the house.

The lord had the evil wife, Kana, killed. He sent for Kana's mother and, without telling her what had happened, gave her the head of her daughter wrapped as a present to take with her when she returned home. On the way home her head began to ache so that she could go no farther. She stopped and unwrapped the package she had received and saw that it contained the head of her daughter. She was so shocked that she fell over in a faint and died.

The lord had another wedding ceremony and married the real Tama-no-Chu. Then, together with Kaniharu, the three of them went to the country of Sashu to visit the lord Sashu. When the father saw both his children well and healthy, he was so happy that he soon recovered from his illness. Kaniharu took a good wife, and so his father had nothing to worry about. The sister and brother continued to help one another, and it is said that they are still living happily until this day.

• *30* • *The Girl without Arms*

Type 706, The Maiden without Hands. *Kata No. 213, "The Girl without Arms." Collected in Yazawa-mura, Hienuki-gun, Iwate-ken, from Sada Odashima.*

This tale is popular in both oral and literary tradition in Europe. Thompson, p. 121, notes that between the twelfth and seventeenth centuries it received seventeen distinct literary handlings, including Chaucer's "The Man of Law's Tale." While

the tale has not been noted in India or China, it is quite popular
in Japan where thirty-three versions have been collected.

No old literary variants are known in Japan, hence the tale
may have been borrowed from Europe within the past two or
three centuries. Ikeda, p. 197, reports that it is a favorite with
wandering storytellers, a fact that may partially account for its
having so thoroughly entered Japanese tradition.

Members of the nobility were required to report periodically
to the shogunate at Edo, a practice instituted by the shogun to
control possible uprisings in outlying provinces. Cf. note to No.
24, "The Fire Boy."

• LONG AGO in a certain place there were a man and his wife
who loved each other very much. They had a beautiful little
daughter; but when she was only four years old, her mother died.
After that her father married again, but her stepmother treated
her very badly, endlessly persecuting her. Her evil stepmother
tried very hard to think of some way of getting rid of her, but
since she was such a well-behaved girl, there was no excuse to
send her away.

The years passed and the girl became fifteen years old, but the
stepmother hated her more and more. "I can't stand that child,"
she thought, and she spent all her time scheming to get rid of her.
One day she said to her husband, "Listen, father, I can't bear to
live with such a clever one as she is; you've got to do something
to get her away from here."

The girl's father always did as the stepmother requested, and
so he replied, "Don't worry; I'll do something to get rid of her."
He immediately agreed to get rid of her even though she had
done nothing wrong.

One day he gave her a beautiful kimono such as she had never
worn before and said, "Let's go to the festival today." The girl
put on the beautiful new kimono, and they set out for the festival. The weather was clear and pleasant, and the girl, who had
never before had a chance to go for a walk with her father, was
overflowing with joy.

They walked and walked, crossing over the top of a mountain.
The girl, wondering why they were traveling so far, asked,

"Father, father, where is the festival being held today?" Her father replied, "We've crossed one mountain, and we must cross another; and there beside the great castle beyond the second mountain, they are holding the festival."

Going on in front, the father led the girl farther and farther into the mountains. They crossed the second mountain, and as they began to descend into the valley, the father suggested that they eat their lunch. They stopped to rest, and taking out the rice balls they had brought with them, they began to eat. After they had eaten, the girl, tired from her long walk, lay down and was soon fast asleep. Seeing that, her father thought to himself, "Now is the time." He took the axe from his belt and cut off the poor girl's arms, first the right, then the left. Leaving her crying in pain, he set off down the mountain alone.

"Oh, father, please wait for me. Father, it hurts so!" Spattered with blood, the girl ran stumbling after him. But her father, without once looking back, hurried on and soon disappeared from view.

"Oh, what shall I do now, even my own father has treated me like this." The poor, homeless girl had no place to go. She came to a river and sat down to wash her wounds. She had no food but wandered about from place to place in the mountains, living on what seeds and berries she could find.

One day a handsome young nobleman's son was out hunting and came riding by with his attendants. He saw the girl hiding in the bushes and called: "What are you? You have a woman's face, but you have no arms."

The girl replied, "My own father did this to me; I am the girl without arms," and breaking into tears, she cried bitterly. The young man asked the reason and upon hearing her story felt so sorry for her that he said, "Well, no matter what has happened to you, you must come home with me." He put her up on his horse with him and turned back down the mountain.

Returning to his home, he called his mother and said: "Mother, I did no hunting today. In the mountains I came upon a girl without arms, and I have brought her home with me. She is so pitiful; please let her stay here," and the young man told everything that had happened to the girl.

The young man's mother was also a kind and loving person. After a maid had washed and powdered the girl's face and combed her hair, the girl without arms was as beautiful as she had ever been. The young man's mother was filled with joy and loved the girl as if she were her real daughter.

A short while after this, the young man said to his mother, "I beg of you, mother, please let me marry this girl." His mother replied, "I, too, was thinking that it would be nice for you to take her as your bride." Since his mother had given her consent, the young man and the girl were soon married.

After some months had passed, it became known that the girl was to give birth to a baby. Before the baby was born, however, the young nobleman found it necessary to go up to Edo. Since his wife and his mother got along so well together, before he left he said, "Mother, please take good care of my wife and baby while I'm gone." His mother replied, "Do not worry; just as soon as the baby is born, we will send a messenger to let you know." Being assured that everything would be taken care of, the young man set off for Edo.

Soon a beautiful baby boy was born, and the grandmother said, "Daughter, let us send word to Edo immediately." She wrote a letter saying that the baby had been born, then called a messenger who lived nearby. She gave him the letter and sent him hurrying up to Edo.

The courier crossed over mountains and through plains; after having traveled a long way, he became very thirsty and stopped at a house along the road to ask for a drink of water. Now it just happened that the place where he stopped was the house where the girl without arms had been born. Her evil stepmother gave the messenger some water to drink and asked him where he was going.

"Oh," he said, "the daughter-in-law of the neighboring nobleman, the girl without arms, has given birth to a child. Since the nobleman's son is in Edo, I am on my way up to give him the news." The unsuspecting messenger told all he knew.

The stepmother, hearing that her stepdaughter was still alive, suddenly began to treat the messenger very kindly. "Such hot weather as this, it's too bad that you have to go up to Edo," she

said. "Why don't you stop and rest a while." Bringing out *sake*
and all sorts of delicious things to eat, she spread them before
him. The messenger soon became quite drunk and fell asleep.
While he was fast asleep, the evil stepmother secretly took the
letter from the box in which it was carried. She opened it and
read:

> Beautiful as a jewel,
> Beautiful beyond compare,
> A son has been born.

When the stepmother read this, she cried, "Oh, how I hate
that girl!" She rewrote the letter to say:

> Ugly as an *oni,*
> Ugly as a snake,
> A *bakemono* has been born.

Then she put the letter back in the courier's box.

When the messenger awoke, he thanked the woman for the
meal, feeling rather foolish about having gotten drunk and fallen
asleep. The stepmother, smiling to herself, said, "On your way
back, be sure to stop again and tell us all the latest gossip from
Edo."

The messenger delivered the letter. When the young nobleman
read it, he was greatly surprised; nevertheless, he sat down and
wrote the following reply:

> Even an *oni,* even a snake,
> Take good care of the child until I return.

Giving the letter to the messenger, he sent him back to his
home. The messenger did not forget that he had been so well
entertained at the house where he had stopped on his way up to
Edo. He decided to stop again on his way back, hoping to be
treated to *sake* and a meal again.

When he stopped at the house, the stepmother called out,
"Are you returning in such hot weather as this? Do come in
and rest a while." She led him into the guest room and gave him
sake and all sorts of food. She kept filling his glass until he was
quite drunk. She waited until he had fallen fast asleep; then she
took the letter he carried and rewrote it to read:

I do not want to see such a baby. I never want to see the girl without arms again. Please send them both away. If you do not do so, I shall never return home but live here in Edo the rest of my life.

She then put it back in the courier's box. When he awoke, he thanked the stepmother and took his leave. He crossed mountains and plains until he returned to the nobleman's house. The young man's mother took the letter; when she opened and read it, she saw that it was not at all what she had expected. "This is a strange letter," she said. "You didn't stop at anyone's house during your journey, did you?"

"No!" he cried. "Of course I stopped nowhere. I went straight as an arrow to Edo, and I returned straight back here."

Even so, the mother thought that she would wait until her son came home. Since he was expected any day, she did not tell her daughter-in-law about the letter.

However as time went on and it appeared that the son was not going to return, the mother, not knowing what else to do, called her daughter-in-law and showed her the letter. "I received this from my son," she said and read it to her. The girl was greatly shocked, but finally she managed to speak. "Mother," she said, "I am a cripple and unable to do anything to repay you for all your kindness. I can hardly bear to leave, but if that is your son's will, there is nothing else to do; I will leave." She asked that the baby be strapped on her back, and taking leave of her mother-in-law, she left the house, crying bitterly.

She started down the road. She had nowhere to go and wandered aimlessly along. Soon she became very thirsty. She came to a small creek and knelt down, thinking that she would get a drink, but the baby on her back began to slip forward and was about to fall off.

"Help me, please! Someone help!" she cried and, forgetting that she had no arms, tried to catch the baby. To her great surprise, she found that both arms had grown back on again, and she was able to catch the baby just in time. "Oh, how happy I am," she cried, "my arms have grown on again." She was nearly beside herself with joy.

A short time after the girl and baby had left, the young nobleman, wanting very much to see his baby, wife, and mother, hurriedly left Edo and returned home. When he learned that his
wife and baby were gone and heard from his mother about
the strange letter which the messenger had brought, he called the
messenger and questioned him closely. He discovered that he
had stopped along the way and that the woman who had made
him drunk was none other than the evil stepmother.

"Oh, the poor girl," his mother cried. "You must go at once
and find her," and she made ready for the young man to leave
immediately.

The young man went to search for his wife, looking everywhere until finally he came to a shrine near a river. There he
saw a beggar woman standing in front of the shrine, holding a
baby in her arms. She was praying earnestly, and as the young
man came up behind her, he thought, "This woman certainly
looks like my wife, but she has both arms, so this could not be
her." However, to make certain, he raised his voice and called to
her. When the woman turned around, it was none other than
his wife. Crying out in joy, the two of them embraced and wept
for happiness.

Strange at it may seem, in the place where their tears fell,
beautiful flowers grew and bloomed, and all along the road as
the three of them returned home together the grass, bushes, and
trees broke out into blossom.

The evil stepmother and the girl's father were afterward punished by the governor of the province for having been so cruel to
their daughter.

Part IV
Kindness Rewarded and Evil Punished

· 31 · *The Good Fortune Kettle*

*Motifs B366, "Animals grateful for release from captivity," and
D612.1, "Illusory transformations of animals in order to sell and
cheat," are applicable here. Kata No. 130, "The Lucky Teakettle." Collected in Tsuchibuchi-mura, Kamihei-gun, Iwate-ken,
from Yonezo Furuyashiki.*

Ikeda assigns this tale to Type 326, The Magician and His
Pupil, *a tale well known throughout Europe and, according to
Thompson, p. 69, now believed to have originated in India.
Thompson notes that Theodor Benfey, in the Prolegomena to
his* Pantschantantra *in 1859, uses this story as an illustration of
the way in which tales from India are taken over into the Mongolian literature and carried through this intermediary into Europe. It is possible that elements of the Indian tale entered Japan
from Mongolian sources.*

*The tale is extremely popular in Japan. It is often used in chil-
dren's books, where, however, the episodes of the sale of the fox
as a prostitute and as a horse are omitted. Children's versions
usually have the fox or the badger, in half-kettle form, become
an entertainer to make money for the old man after escaping
from the priest.*

*It was a common practice in feudal Japan, and even in modern
Japan until the recent outlawing of prostitution, for poverty-
stricken parents to sell a daughter to a house of prostitution.*

• IN A CERTAIN place there lived an old man and his wife. They
were very poor. The old man would go to the mountains every-
day and cut firewood, then take it to the village and sell it; and
that is how they lived from day to day.

One day when the old man went to the mountains as usual,
he saw that three of the village boys had caught a fox and were
about to kill it. He scolded the boys, saying, "Here, here, what
are you boys doing; you shouldn't be treating an animal so
cruelly. Why don't you sell it to me?" And he gave each of them
one hundred *mon*.

The boys were delighted and cried, "Really! Then we will sell it to you," and they handed over the end of the rope which was around the fox's neck.

"Oh, how pitiful, how pitiful," said the old man as he led the fox to the mountains. "I don't know which mountain you have come from, but after this you shouldn't go near the village in broad daylight. You must be careful not to be caught by those boys again. Now you'd better hurry back to your den," and he carefully let the fox loose in the middle of a thicket.

The next day the old man went again to the mountains. There the fox from the day before came up to him and said: "Grandfather, grandfather, you saved my life yesterday when I was in great danger; I am more thankful than I can tell."

"Why, are you the fox I helped yesterday!" said the old man. "I didn't expect to receive anything from you for that; that isn't why I helped you. You looked so pitiful that I wanted to help you, but I don't need any reward for it. You are only an animal, and you've said thank you; that is plenty. But more important than that, if you come out in a place like this, the boys from the village will catch you again. Now hurry and go back to your den."

The fox, tears falling from its eyes, crept up to the old man and said, "Grandfather, grandfather, I've something to tell you. At the temple in the village below here they have no teakettle, but they want one very badly. Now I will turn myself into a kettle, and although it will be rather heavy, you must take the kettle and sell it to the priest. This way you will get some money. Will you do that, grandfather?" Then the fox curled his tail around himself, whirled around and around three times, and turned into a splendid copper kettle. The old man tapped the rim of the kettle, and it rang, *go-on,* with a good metallic clang.

Since the fox had turned himself into the kettle, the old man couldn't very well just leave it there, so he put it on his shoulders and went to the temple. "This kettle belonged to my ancestors, but now I must sell it," he said. As soon as the priest saw it, he wanted to have it.

"It is a valuable kettle; please let me have it for this," said the priest and gave the old man three *ryo.*

The old man had never seen so much money before. He put the three *ryo* in his purse and returned home full of joy.

The priest was delighted to have a kettle he liked so much. He called the temple acolytes and said, "Take this kettle and polish it with sand. We will have a stovemaker come tomorrow and make us a stove."

The acolytes rolled the kettle around to the back door and, taking some sand, began polishing it vigorously, *goshi goshi,* scratch scratch. When they did that, the kettle cried, "Boys, it hurts me! Boys, it hurts me! Please polish softly."

The acolytes were greatly surprised and ran into the temple kitchen, shouting, "Priest-*sama,* priest-*sama,* that kettle talks!"

"What!" said the priest. "That is just the ringing sound the kettle makes; it just sounded like words to you. It is a good kettle, and it has various kinds of sounds. But if you want to, bring it back to the kitchen and leave it there." The acolytes were still a bit fearful but did as the priest had said. They rolled the kettle from the river bank back up to the kitchen and left it there.

That night the kettle disappeared; not a trace of it could be found anywhere. The priest was greatly disappointed, saying over and over again that since it was such a good kettle a thief must have come during the night and stolen it.

The old man, knowing nothing of what had happened, went to the mountains again the next day. There he again met the fox who said: "Good morning, grandfather. Yesterday, at that temple, the acolytes used sand to polish me, and I really got some rough treatment. Today I will turn myself into your daughter. Please go to town and buy combs, a set of hair ornaments, a sash, towels, an apron, and some *tabi* for me. If you do that, I will become a beautiful girl, and you can take me to the house of prostitution in town and sell me for a lot of money. Please hurry, please hurry."

Since the fox had asked him to, the old man set off immediately for town and bought the things he had been requested to get; then he returned to the mountains.

"Grandfather, you came back so soon!" cried the fox. "And I like everything you bought very much! Oh, how interesting!

Now I will turn myself into a girl, so please watch." Saying this, the fox whirled around three times and turned into a beautiful young girl.

The old man took the girl and went with her to the house of prostitution in the town. "This is my daughter," he said. "Would you like to buy her?" The owner of the house wanted the girl, and so he gave the old man one hundred *ryo* for her. Taking the bag of money, the old man returned home. At the house of prostitution the girl became very popular and earned her master a great deal of money.

The next year, at one of the holidays, the girl went to the master and said: "Since I have come here, I have not been home to see my parents at all; I would like to go and see them now. Please, may I have one day off?"

The master realized that what she said was true. He gave her a great number of presents for her parents, and she left for her home village. After that she never went back to the house of prostitution. The master said that the girl had already made many times more money for him than he had paid for her, and if she were tired of being a prostitute, there was nothing he could do about it; so he did not even send anyone to bring her back.

The old man went to the mountains one day, and the fox again came up to him and said: "Grandfather, grandfather, we haven't met for a long time. Are you well? I have been at the house of prostitution in town, but I got tired of it, and so I have been resting. I have almost completely recuperated now, and so I would like to repay your kindness one more time. This time I shall become a horse. Please take the horse to a rich man in some distant country and sell it. This is the very best thing that I can do for you. If things go badly for me, I may never see you again; so if that happens, please observe today as the anniversary of my death. Please think of me once in a while and burn some incense for me. Well, now I shall become a horse."

"Please stop!" cried the old man. "You have taken care of me time after time, and I no longer live so poorly as before. I have everything I need. You do not need to do anything more for me." But even as the old man was talking, the fox became a splendid gray horse. Since there was nothing else the old man could do, he took the horse to a rich man in a distant country and sold it for one hundred *ryo;* then he took the money and returned home.

Shortly after this there was to be a festival. The gray horse who had been a fox was saddled with a huge chest upon which a nobleman rode, and they set off across a long, long mountain pass. Despite his appearance, the gray horse was still actually a fox. He soon reached the end of his strength and could go no further. A crowd of men saw this and called out, "See what happens when a horse is not used to such work."

Soon the fox-horse fell in its tracks. "This horse is good for nothing," they cried and threw it into a swamp. They transferred the nobleman and the baggage onto another horse and continued across the mountain. After they had all left, the fox-horse got up and went off somewhere. He was never seen again.

Having become rich because of the fox's kindness, the old man became known in the neighborhood as the Happiness and Prosperity *Choja.* The old man never forgot the fox's last wish; in his mansion he built a splendid chapel where on the nineteenth day of every month he and the old woman would go and pray for the fox's rebirth in paradise.

∙32∙ Urashima Taro

Motif D2011, "Years thought days," is prominent in this tale. Kata No. 167, "Urashima Taro." Collected on Sayagi Island, Nakatado-gun, Kagawa-ken, from Sotaro Wada.

This tale is widely distributed throughout Japan. It is one of the dozen or so tales constantly reprinted in children's books. The oldest known variant of the tale is found in the eighth-century quasi-historical record, the Nihongi, *p. 368, where it is told as having occurred in the year* A.D. *477 to a fisherman named Urashima of the province of Tanba in southwestern Japan.*

When first introduced into the United States in the late nineteenth century, this tale was called the Japanese Rip Van Winkle. Lafcadio Hearn, as lecturer in English and American litera-

ture in Tokyo University, was instrumental in acquainting the Japanese with Washington Irving's literary reworking of the motif "Years thought days."

Mirrors have a religious significance in Shinto ritual and are often endowed with magical properties. Urashima's glance into the mirror and transformation into a crane, a symbol of longevity, is in keeping with his having lived many centuries in the undersea kingdom. However, in many versions of this tale, Urashima merely turns into an old man and dies upon opening the box, which contains only a puff of smoke.

The Crane and Turtle Dance is a traditional dance of the region around Ise, location of the oldest and most important Shinto shrine.

• LONG AGO a man named Urashima Taro lived at Kitamae Oshima. He lived with his mother, who was nearly eighty years old. He was a fisherman and was still unmarried. One day his mother said to him, "Urashima, Urashima, while I still have my health, won't you please take a bride."

"I am as yet unable to earn a living. Even if I took a bride, I could not support her; while you are still living, I shall continue fishing and go on living like this," he said.

The days and months passed, and the mother became eighty years old. Urashima was forty. It was autumn, and the north wind blew day after day so that it was impossible to go out to fish. Since he could catch no fish, he could make no money, and it began to appear that he would be unable even to get food for his mother. "Ah, if we could only have good weather tomorrow," he thought, as he lay around with nothing to do.

Suddenly the sky began to clear. Urashima Taro jumped up, climbed onto his raft, and set out to fish. He fished until it began to get light in the east, but he could not catch a single fish. He was greatly troubled, but as the sun rose higher in the sky, a large fish finally struck the hook. Quickly he hauled in the line and found that he had caught a turtle. The turtle clung to the edge of the raft and made no move to go away.

"I thought maybe you were a sea bream, but you are only a turtle. Since you're here, no other fish will take the hook. Here,

I'll take you off the hook; now please go away somewhere," said Urashima, throwing the turtle back into the sea.

Urashima lighted his pipe and smoked as he continued fishing, but he caught nothing. He was greatly troubled, but just before noon it again felt as if a large fish had struck the hook. He hauled it in, and it was the turtle again. "No matter how much I ask him to go away, the turtle keeps coming back and the fish won't bite. I'm having very bad luck," he said and again chased the turtle away. Since he could not return home with nothing at all, he patiently kept fishing until mid-afternoon, when again something struck the hook. Thinking that surely this time it must be a fish, he hauled in the line and saw that it was the turtle again; so again he chased it away. It kept on like this until the sun began to set, and he had not caught a single fish. Soon the sun sank from sight, and he started home, wondering what to say to his mother.

He was paddling the raft along when he noticed a seagoing ship in the distance. For some reason or other it was coming toward him. Urashima steered his boat to starboard, and the ship did the same; he steered to port, and the seagoing ship also steered to port. Finally the ship came alongside Urashima's boat. The captain called out, "Urashima, please come on board this ship; we have come to you from the princess of Ryugu [the dragon kingdom at the bottom of the sea].

"If I went to the dragon kingdom, my mother would be all alone, so I cannot go."

"We will see that your mother is well taken care of; please come on board our ship," urged the captain, and so Urashima, without further thought, boarded the ship.

As soon as Urashima was on board, the ship sank into the water and went to the world at the bottom of the sea. When Urashima arrived, he saw that there was a beautiful palace there; the princess came and, saying that he surely must be hungry, gave him a feast. "Please stay two or three days and enjoy yourself," she said. "Then you can return home."

Urashima saw that the princess and many other beautiful young girls were there; he was given new kimonos, and in this way days and months passed without his noticing, until three years had gone by. Urashima felt that he must return home. When he asked the princess if he might go, she gave him a three-tiered jewel box. "In case of necessity, you may open the box," she said. Then Urashima was put on board the seagoing ship, and they landed at a place similar to this one here, which looks like a mountain's nose.

Urashima went to his village and looked around, but even the face of the mountain had changed; the trees on the hills had died or disappeared. "How could all this have happened in only three years?" he thought to himself as he went to where his house was. There in a thatched house was an old man working with straw. Urashima entered the house, greeted the old man, and inquired about himself, asking, "Do you know a man by the name of Urashima?"

The old man replied, "There was a story that in my grandfather's time a man named Urashima went to the dragon kingdom at the bottom of the sea, but no matter how long his relatives waited, he never returned."

"What became of that man's mother?" asked Urashima and was told that she had died long, long ago.

Urashima went to see the remains of his own house. Only the stone wash basin and the garden steppingstones remained; other than that, there was nothing. Lost in reverie, he opened the lid of the box; in the first box there was a crane's feather. He opened the next box, and a puff of white smoke came from it; at this Urashima was turned into an old man. In the third box there was a mirror. He looked in the mirror and saw to his surprise that he had become an old man.

While he was looking in the mirror, the crane's feather from the first box attached itself to his back. He flew up into the sky and circled around his mother's grave. When he did this, the princess from the sea, who had turned herself into a turtle, came up on the beach to see him.

It is said that this is the origin of the Crane and Turtle Dance at Ise.

The Tongue-cut Sparrow

Type 480, The Spinning-Women by the Spring. The Kind and the Unkind Girls. Kata No. 239, "The Tongue-cut Sparrow." Collected in Nishitani-mura, Enuma-gun, Ishikawa-ken, by Hisao Yamashita.

This tale is popular throughout Japan, with thirty-five variants recorded from oral tradition. It is often included in children's books as an example of the disastrous consequences of cruelty and greed. It was printed again and again in the eighteenth century and has been drastically retouched in the literary versions, most of which do not include the encounters with various informants for whom the old man must perform tasks.

Roberts, in his exhaustive study of The Tale of the Kind and the Unkind Girls, *analyzed twenty-three Japanese variants along with some nine hundred versions from more than fifty countries throughout the world. He concluded, p. 139, that the tale is essentially of Near Eastern origin and has spread to Japan from that area.*

The significance of drinking the water in which animals and vegetables had been washed is not clear. It may have been a task designed to test the old man's willingness to atone for his wife's cruelty.

• WELL, THIS was long ago. There were an old man and his wife. One day the old man went to the mountains to cut firewood. When he got there he hung his lunch on the branch of a tree, and a sparrow came along and ate it up. When the old man got ready to eat his lunch, he unwrapped it and found the sparrow in it, asleep. He took the sparrow and cared for it. He named it Ochon.

One day the old man left the sparrow with the old woman and went to the mountains to cut firewood. Since it was a nice day, the old woman decided to do her washing, and so she made some starch. She said to the sparrow, "I am going to the river to do the washing; you watch the starch so that the neighbor's cat doesn't get into it," and she went off to the river.

The sparrow became very hungry, so it ate up all the starch. When the old woman returned from the river, she asked, "Ochon, Ochon, what happened to the starch?"

"The neighbor's cat ate it," replied the sparrow.

The old woman looked in the neighbor's cat's mouth, but there was no trace of starch there. Then she looked in the sparrow's mouth, and there was some starch stuck in its mouth. She cut out the sparrow's tongue and drove the poor sparrow out of the house.

Soon the old man returned from the mountains and asked "Where is Ochon?"

"I made some starch," said the old woman, "but while I was at the river, the sparrow ate it up. I got angry and cut out its tongue and drove it away."

The old man felt sorry for the sparrow and went off to hunt for it, calling out,

> Where has Ochon the sparrow gone?
> Where has the tongue-cut sparrow gone?
> The poor little thing, where has he gone?

He went for some distance and came to a man who was washing cows. "Cow-washer-*sama*, cow-washer-*sama*, a tongue-cut sparrow didn't come by here, did he?"

"He came by, he came by. If you'll drink the cow's wash water, out of father's bowl filled thirteen times and out of mother's bowl filled thirteen times, I'll tell you where he went."

The old man drank the cow's wash water and was told, "Go on down the road and you will come to a horse-washer."

> Where has the tongue-cut sparrow gone?
> Where has Ochon the sparrow gone?
> The poor little thing, the poor little thing!

Singing this song, the old man went along for some way and came to a horse-washer. "Horse-washer-*sama*, horse-washer-*sama*, a tongue-cut sparrow didn't come by here, did he?"

"He came by, he came by. If you'll drink the horse's wash

water, out of father's bowl filled thirteen times and out of mother's bowl filled thirteen times, I'll tell you where he went."

The old man drank the horse's wash water and was told, "Go on down the road and you will come to a greens-washer."

> Where has Ochon the sparrow gone?
> Where has the tongue-cut sparrow gone?
> The poor little thing, the poor little thing!

The old man went for some way and came to a greens-washer. "Greens-washer-*sama*, greens-washer-*sama*, a tongue-cut sparrow didn't come by here, did he?"

"He came by, he came by. If you'll drink the water I washed the greens in, out of mother's bowl filled thirteen times and out of father's bowl filled thirteen times, I'll tell you where he went."

The old man drank the water the greens had been washed in, and the greens-washer said, "Go on down this road and you will come to a large bamboo grove. Go into the grove, and there the sparrow will be. He will have on a red apron and a red *tasuki* [sleeve binder] and will be cutting rice."

> Where has the tongue-cut sparrow gone?
> Where has Ochon the sparrow gone?
> The poor little thing, the poor little thing!

The old man sang this song as he went along. He went for quite some way and finally came to a large bamboo grove. He went into the grove and soon came to the sparrow's house. He knocked at the door, and a voice called, "Is it grandfather or grandmother?"

"It's grandfather, it's grandfather."

"Then if it's grandfather, come right on in."

When the old man went in, he was given a feast and was well entertained. Then the sparrow asked, "Would you like to have a heavy trunk or a light one?"

"I am getting old; I would rather have the light one," he said, and so the light trunk was put on the old man's shoulders. "You must not open this until you get home. Then you may open it," he was told.

When the old man got home, he opened the trunk and found

to his and the old woman's joy that it was full of *oban* and *koban* coins.

The old woman was very greedy and said: "I shall go and get some too." She set off, and when she got to the sparrow's place, she knocked on the door. A voice came, "Is it grandfather or grandmother?"

"It's grandmother, it's grandmother."

"Then if it's grandmother, come right on in."

The old woman went in and instead of a tray, she was served on a board from the toilet. Sticks were broken off the fence for her to use as chopsticks, and she was given sand instead of rice.

When the old woman was ready to leave, she was asked, "Grandmother, would you rather have a heavy basket or a light one?" Since she was very greedy, she replied that she would take the heavy one. "Then take it on your shoulders and do not look inside until you get home," the sparrow said.

The old woman wanted to peek in the basket, so she went behind the fence and opened it up. When she did that, snakes and vipers and scorpions came out and stung the old woman to death.

We should not be greedy.

•*34*• *The Old Man Who Cut Bamboo*

Motifs D2063.5, "Magic discomfort, continued breaking of wind," and Q262, "Impostor punished," are pertinent here. Kata No. 238, "The Old Man Who Cut Bamboo." Collected in Toyonemura, Kitashidara-gun, Aichi-ken, by Hiroyuki Sasaki.

Ikeda, p. 150, assigns this tale to Type 480, the tale type discussed immediately above. Roberts, in his study of the type, felt that many of the numerous Japanese tales containing the motif of unsuccessful imitation did not belong to Type 480, and he did not use them in his study.

This tale is very common in the oral tradition of Japan, more than one hundred versions having been collected. Dorson, in Folk Legends of Japan, *gives a somewhat simplified version, "The*

Old Man Who Broke Wind," pp. 207-8, in which there is no mention of punishment of the second old man. The motif of magic breaking of wind has been noted in a Cheremis tale from southern Russia and in a tale collected in North Carolina.

The bird's song appears to be onomatopoetic from the sound of breaking wind. See No. 49, "The Golden Eggplant," for the story of a woman who was banished for breaking wind in her husband's presence.

• LONG, LONG ago in a certain place there lived an old man. One day he went to till his fields, and a tit came and perched on his hoe handle. The old man grabbed him and swallowed him in one bite. The bird's legs, however, stuck out his anus, and when he tried to pull them out, the bird in his stomach sang,

> *Chin chin kuri kuri*
> *Pon pon kuri kuri*
> *Koma sara sara.*

The old man returned home and told his wife about it. She said that if he went to the lord's bamboo grove and cut some bamboo, brought it home, and heated up the bath, perhaps the bird would come out. So the old man went to the lord's bamboo grove and cut some bamboo. Just as he was doing this, the lord came riding by.

"Who is that cutting bamboo there?" he demanded angrily.

"The old man who breaks wind," answered the old man.

"If you can break wind, try it once," the lord said.

The old man rolled up his kimono and pulled the bird's legs, and the sound came,

> *Chin chin kuri kuri*
> *Pon pon kuri kuri*
> *Koma sara sara.*

"Well, that is interesting; do it again," said the lord. The old man pulled the bird's legs again, and it sang,

> *Chin chin kuri kuri*
> *Pon pon kuri kuri*
> *Koma sara sara.*

The lord was very impressed. He gave the old man many, many gifts and said that he could cut all the bamboo he wanted.

A neighboring old man, who was very greedy, heard about this. He said, "I shall go too," and so he went to the lord's bamboo grove and cut some bamboo. Just then the lord again came by. "Who is that cutting bamboo?" he asked.

"The old man who breaks wind," the greedy old man answered.

"If you can break wind, try it once."

The greedy old man rolled up his kimono and grunted with all his might, but instead of breaking wind, something more dirty came out.

The lord became very angry. He pulled out his sword and cut off the old man's buttocks.

The greedy old man's wife was at home waiting for the old man to return, wondering what sort of gifts he would bring, when just then she saw him coming in the distance with his buttocks cut off. She thought that he had received a great number of gifts and was riding a horse. "With all those beautiful gifts, we should not have so many rags lying around the house," she thought, so she took them all and burned them in the stove.

Just then the old man returned. "Old woman, I need some rags," he said.

"I thought you were coming riding a red horse, so I burned all the old rags," said the old woman.

·35· The Old Man Who Made Flowers Bloom

Motif Q2, "Kind and unkind," and Q262, "Impostor punished," are central in this tale. Kata No. 236, "The Old Man Who Caught Wild Ducks." Collected in Ota-mura, Kami Niikawagun, Toyama-ken, by Eitaro Ota.

This is another tale about unsuccessful imitation assigned by Ikeda to Type 480, but not used by Roberts in his detailed

study of that tale type. The story is one of the dozen or so peren-
nials included in children's books and is widely known through-
out Japan. It has a vigorous oral tradition, with sixty-four col-
lected versions. A legend in which a magic mortar and pestle is
used by both a good old man and a bad old man with results ap-
propriate to their characters is given by Dorson, in Folk Legends
of Japan, *pp. 190–91. The motif of producing flowers by scattering*
ashes seems to be unique to Japan, although the magic properties
of ashes are recognized in the folk traditions of many countries.

Some versions of this tale have the kind old man accidentally
discover that the ashes will cause trees to bloom. The variant
given here implies that he was aware that the ashes of the magic
millstone would retain magical properties.

The names Taro and Jiro are very common names for boys.
The eldest boy is sometimes named Taro; Jiro indicates "second
boy."

The oban, koban, nibu, and isshu coins were the four most
valuable coin denominations. The koban was one-tenth of an
oban; nibu and isshu were one-half and one-fourth, respectively,
of a koban.

• IT IS SAID that this once happened.

Long, long ago in a certain place there lived an old man and
an old woman. The old man went to the mountains to cut firewood, and the old woman went to the river to wash clothes.
While she was washing clothes, a huge peach came bobbing and
floating, *ponpoko ponkoko,* down the river.

"Let another one come and I'll give it to Taro; let still another
one come and I'll give it to Jiro," said the old woman. She picked
up the peach, took it home with her, and put it in the big pounding mortar.

Soon the old man returned from the mountains. "Old woman,
old woman, is there anything to eat?" he asked. "Yes, as I was
washing clothes in the river, a huge peach came floating down
the river. I put it in the mortar in the storeroom. You can get it
and eat it," said the old woman.

"Ah, how delicious that should be. I'll have some of it," said
the old man and went to get it. When he got to the storeroom,

he was very surprised, more surprised than he had ever been before in his life. "Old woman, old woman, you said that this was a peach, but it is a young puppy," he cried with a look of amazement on his face.

Now it really was a puppy. The old woman said, "But I know that it was a peach that I brought from the river."

"Well, no matter what, it is a puppy now," said the old man, and they both looked at it carefully and saw that it surely was a puppy. They kept it and cared for it very carefully, and it gradually grew bigger and bigger.

One day the dog spoke to the old man, "Grandfather, grandfather, please put a saddle on me."

"You are not strong enough to carry a saddle; I couldn't do that."

"It is all right; please put one on me."

The old man put a saddle on him, and then the dog said, "Grandfather, grandfather, please tie a straw bag on me."

"You are not strong enough; I couldn't tie a straw bag on you."

"It is all right; please tie one on me."

The old man tied a straw bag on the dog's back, and then the dog said, "Grandfather, grandfather, please tie a hoe on me."

"You are not strong enough; I couldn't tie a hoe on you."

"It's all right; please tie one on me."

Next the dog said, "Now follow me," and so the old man followed him. They went a long way into the mountains, and the dog said, "Old man, dig here." The old man took the hoe and the straw bag from the dog's back and began to dig. He dug for a while and soon had dug up a great number of *koban* and *oban* and *nibu* and *isshu* coins.

"Please put them in the straw bag and tie them on my back," said the dog.

The old man was overjoyed at the find but said, "You are not strong enough; I will carry them," but the dog said. "It is all right; please tie them on my back."

The old man tied the straw bag on the dog's back, and then the dog said, "Grandfather, grandfather, please ride on my back.

"You are not strong enough; I couldn't ride on your back," said the old man.

"It's all right; please get on," said the dog. The old man got on, and they galloped, *tontoko tontoko,* down the mountain. When they got home, he spread the contents of the bag out in the storeroom and began to count the *koban* and *oban* coins, when just then an old woman neighbor came over to borrow a hot coal to start her fire.

"Old man, old man," she said, "you are always saying that you have no money; where did you get such a lot of it?"

The old man told her everything that had happened, from the beginning to the end. The old woman said, "If he is such a good dog, please loan him to us for a day." The old man readily agreed and loaned her the dog.

When the dog was taken over to the neighbor's house, it again said, "Old man, old man, tie a straw bag on my back." Now the old man and the old woman were very greedy and said, "We borrowed you just so that we could tie a bag on your back." Then when the dog asked them to tie a hoe on his back and then get on and ride, the old man said, "We borrowed you in order to tie a hoe on you," and, "just so I could ride you."

So, with the old man riding, the dog set off for the mountains. They went for some way; then the dog said, "Dig here." The old man took the hoe and began to dig, but he was very surprised to find that he could dig up nothing but huge snakes, frogs, centipedes, and all sorts of disgusting things like that. He became very angry and cried, "You worthless beast, why did you tell me to dig here?" Finally he killed the dog. He buried him beside that place and stuck a willow branch over the grave.

At home, the old man's wife was waiting for him to return, sure that he would be bringing the straw bag full of *oban* and *koban* coins, but when he came he looked very disgusted. "Old man, old man," she asked, "what is the matter?"

"You ask me what is the matter. Well, I'll tell you what's the matter. That dog was supposed to tell me where to dig—well he told me where to dig all right; right in the most disgusting spot!" When he told what had happened, the old woman, too, was very surprised.

Meanwhile the old man from whom they had borrowed the dog was saying, "I wonder what has happened to the dog we loaned our neighbor this morning; he hasn't returned it yet," and he went over to the neighboring old man's place to ask about it. There the old man angrily told him what had happened.

"Oh, what a pitiful thing to have done; you've killed my dog," he said. The next day he went to where the willow branch was stuck in the ground. When he got there, he saw that the little branch that had been stuck in the ground had grown up to be a big willow tree. The old man decided to cut down the willow tree and make a hand mill out of it as a memento of the dog.

When he and the old woman began to turn the hand mill, they were very surprised to find that in front of the old man *oban* coins came out and that in front of the old woman *koban* coins came out.

While they were turning the hand mill, the neighboring old woman again came over to borrow some coals to start her fire. "Where did you get all this money?" she asked.

"The willow which your old man stuck up where our dog was buried had grown into a large tree, so we took it and made a hand mill out of it. When we started grinding with it, all this money came out."

"Really! Well then, loan us the hand mill for a day, will you?"

"Please take it if you wish," they said.

The greedy old woman and the greedy old man borrowed the hand mill and began to turn it. When they did that, a terrible thing happened. In front of the old man, horse dung came out and in front of the woman cow dung came out. They became very angry. They took the hand mill and cut it up, then burned it in their fireplace.

The hand mill had not been returned, so the old man who had made it went to get it. The neighboring old man said, "That hand mill threw out horse dung in front of me and cow dung in front of my wife, and so we got angry and burned it up in the fireplace.

"What a terrible thing you have done. Anyway, do you still have the ashes?"

"I suppose they might be in a corner of the fireplace," said the neighboring old man, grudgingly.

The old man took the ashes and returned home with them. He climbed up in a tree and called out, "I am Japan's number-one ash-scattering old man!" Just then a splendid samurai passed by. He called, "Who are you up there?"

"I am Japan's number-one ash-scattering old man!"

"Then let's see you scatter some."

The old man scattered some of the ashes, and beautiful plum and cherry blossoms began to appear on the trees. The samurai praised him highly and gave him a great deal of money; then he went on his way.

As the old man and the old woman were counting the money, the neighboring old woman again came over to borrow some fire. "Where did all that money come from?" she asked.

"My old man took the ashes that he had gotten from your place and was scattering them from up in a tree, when just then a samurai came along. The old man scattered ashes for him, and he thought it was so pretty that he gave us all this money." The greedy old woman then asked to borrow the ashes and went home.

The greedy old woman told her husband to climb up in a tree and wait with the ashes until a samurai came by. He did so, and soon a samurai came by. He asked, "Who is that up there?"

"I am Japan's number-one ash-scattering old man."

"Then let's see you scatter some."

"Now I shall certainly be rewarded," thought the old man and began to scatter the ashes; but instead of beautiful flowers appearing, the ashes flew into the samurai's eyes, and he became very angry.

And so we must not try to imitate other people.

Katattemo kataraidemo sooroo. "No matter whether it is told or not, that is the way it happened."

· 36 · *The Old Men Who Had Wens*

Type 503, The Gifts of the Little People. Kata No. 241, "The Old Men Who Had Wens." Collected in Tsuchibuchi-mura, Kamihei-gun, Iwate-ken, from Tanie Haneishi.

Thompson, p. 49, refers to a fourteenth-century Arabic literary story containing the motif of transferred humps and states that the tale as it is known in Europe appeared in the literature of seventeenth-century Italy and Ireland. The fact that it appears in the Uji Shui, a thirteenth-century Japanese collection, would indicate that the origin of the tale is even more obscure than has been supposed. Twenty-five texts are known in oral tradition in Japan. It is widely used in children's books, often to point a moral of the contrasting characters of the two old men; one is kind and good, the other evil and greedy.

• LONG, LONG ago there were two old men who each had a wen as big as one's fist. They felt that it was an awful thing to have such unsightly wens, so they went far back in the mountains to a shrine to ask the deities if the wens could be taken off. There they sat up every night praying.

One night, just at midnight, they heard a sound coming from far in the distance. It gradually came closer, and as they listened carefully, they could tell that it was the sound of flutes and drums. While they were wondering what was going to happen, the sound came up to the outer gate of the shrine.

> Torere, torere,
> Tohyara, tohyara,
> Sutoton, sutoton.

The sound of the music came so close that it could be heard clearly, even in the main hall of the shrine. Thinking that something dreadful might happen to them, the two old men decided to creep into one corner of the shrine and try to hide themselves. Just as they were hidden, the door of the shrine burst open and a group of five or six *tengu* [mischievous ogres] came in. They appeared to be over six *shaku* [about six feet] tall, with bright red faces and long noses.

> *Torere, torere,*
> *Tohyara, tohyara,*
> *Sutoton, sutoton.*

The *tengu* continued their music. However, with only music and no one dancing, they appeared to be getting bored and began urging one another to dance. But none of them knew any dances.

One of the *tengu* became provoked and started to turn away in disgust. As he did this, he happened to spy the two old men. "Oh ho!" he cried, "there are some men here. Since you're here, why don't you come out and dance for us. Hurry up, come on." He took one of them by the sleeve and pushed him out into the circle of *tengu*.

The old man was trembling with fright, but the music was lively, and he soon fell into step and began a merry dance, singing,

> The walnut pops open, pop! Pop!
> The baby is frightened
> And looks for its mother.
> *Chiya aruruu sutten gaa* [imitating sound of music].

And so he danced, singing this song three times over. The *tengu* were delighted and clapped their hands, showering him with praise.

"You danced so well," they said, "it's a shame you have that ugly wen on your forehead. The way it is now, we can't tell what you look like. You are such a good dancer we'll take it off for you." Saying this, the *tengu* removed the wen from the old man's forehead so that there was not a trace of it left. The old man felt his head suddenly relieved of the heavy wen and sat down filled with happiness.

Next they took the other old man and pushed him out into the middle of the circle. "Now it is your turn; do a dance for us," they cried. Taking up their flutes and drums, they began the accompaniment,

> *Torere, torere,*
> *Tohyara, tohyara,*
> *Sutoton, sutoton.*

The old man was so frightened that he trembled until his bones rattled, but try as he might, his knees refused to move. The *tengu* began to cough ominously. He knew that he had to do something, and he began to dance, singing this song,

> It rains and rains and rains.
> Oh, when it rains how sad it seems.
> *Karoran tomo sutten gaa* [imitating sound of music].

However, even though he was singing, his voice was quavering and his teeth were chattering so that he was sadly out of tune. Besides that, his voice got so low that the *tengu*, who were boisterous fellows, cried out in disgust, "Louder, sing louder." But the old man became more and more frightened and finally fell flat on his rump and burst out crying.

The *tengu* became very angry. They shouted, "There's a limit even to timidity! Are our faces so funny that you have to be that frightened? Here we play good music for you and you just sit there and cry. We hope we never meet anyone like you again! Here, you can have this wen too!" Picking up the wen they had removed from the other old man's face, they slapped it on his face, right on top of his nose.

The old man, taken by surprise, felt his nose; there was another huge wen, just below the one he had always had. Now his face was truly awful looking, so that no one ever wanted to look at him again.

·37· *The Monkeys' Jizo-sama*

Related to Type 503, The Gifts of the Little People. Kata No. 242, "The Monkey Jizo." Collected in Fukuoka-mura, Esashi-gun, Iwate-ken, from Masuji Kikuchi.

This tale is common in Japanese oral tradition, forty-seven examples being known. No really close analogues are found outside of Japan. The plot is similar to Type 503 in that the greed of the

*second old man brings about his punishment. An introductory
element in a tale recorded in Zong In-sob's Folktales from Korea,
pp. 129-36, contains the episode of a man being carried by non-
human beings, while pretending that he is unconscious. He is
punished for his deception after it is discovered.*

*When visiting a shrine, it is customary to toss a few coins into
a box provided for this purpose. The monkeys were imitating
this practice by throwing coins at the foot of the Jizo statue.*

• AN OLD MAN lived in a certain place. His wife made him some
roasted buckwheat *mochi,* and he went to the mountain fields to
cut grass. As he was working, a group of monkeys came, took the
old man's lunch which he had hung on the branch of a tree, and
ate all the roasted buckwheat *mochi.* Even at that the old man just
sat in the middle of the field and watched, saying nothing. The
monkeys spied the old man and cried, "Why, here is a statue of
Jizo-*sama.* It's a shame to leave it here in the middle of the field;
let's take it and let it guard the temple over across the river." So
they all made a chair by joining their hands. They put the old
man in it; then singing this song,

> The monkeys may be dirty,
> But Jizo-*sama* doesn't get dirty,

they waded across the river. The old man thought the whole
thing very funny, but he kept his eyes closed and said nothing
at all. Finally they took him up to the temple on the mountain
and set him down in the place of honor. Then they took a great
number of coins which they had found somewhere and, bringing them one by one, they threw them down at the old man's
feet as an offering. After they had done this, they all ran off
and disappeared.

After the monkeys had all gone, the old man leisurely picked
up all the coins and left the temple. He went to the nearby town
and bought some beautiful kimonos and so forth, then returned
home.

The old man and the old woman put on their new clothes
and were just sitting down to enjoy a delicious feast when the
neighboring old woman came over. "Where did you get all
those beautiful kimonos and things; what are you celebrating?"

she asked. The old man and his wife told her the reason, and she said, "Then I shall have my husband do the same thing, so he can get some too," and she hurried home.

The neighboring old man did as his wife told him; taking some roasted buckwheat *mochi,* he went to the mountains. He hung his lunch up on the branch of a tree and waited until a group of monkeys came and ate it up. The monkeys saw the old man in the middle of the field, sitting like a Jizo-*sama;* so they made a chair with their hands, put him in it, and then, singing this song,

> The monkeys may be dirty,
> But Jizo-*sama* doesn't get dirty,

started across the river. The old man thought the song so funny that without thinking he burst out laughing and opened his eyes just as they were in the middle of the river. The monkeys were surprised and, unclasping their hands, dumped the old man right into the river.

The old man went bobbing, *tsunbuku kanbu,* down the river. Finally he managed to grab hold of a willow growing by the river. By holding onto this he could crawl up on the bank. All this time the old woman was at home, waiting for the old man to get the money from the monkeys so she could go and buy beautiful kimonos and such things. She thought he would be coming soon, so she took the clothes that she was wearing, burned them, and waited with nothing on for the old man to return. Soon she heard the old man crying, *ooi ooi,* as he came home, soaking wet as a rat. "There is the old man singing a song as he comes with the beautiful kimonos and money he received from the monkeys!" cried the old woman as she waited for him to arrive.

• 38 • *Benizara and Kakezara*

Type 510A, Cinderella. *Kata No. 210, "Komebuku and Awa-buku," and No. 211, "Dish Dish Mountain." Collected in Hama-matsu City, Shizuoka-ken, by Hana Watanabe.*

This variant of the well-known Cinderella tale is one of a number of related stepmother tales found in Japan. Marian Cox's 1893 study of the Cinderella cycle was the first extensive investigation ever made of a folktale. The cycle was restudied in 1952 by Anna Birgitta Rooth, who used over nine hundred versions from Europe and Asia. Neither of these studies made use of the some thirty-seven versions of the tale which have been recorded in Japan, and so the relationship of the Japanese tradition to that of China, India, and Europe remains to be clarified.

Ikeda, p. 163, reports that a nineteenth-century Kabuki drama about two sisters known as Red-dish and Chipped-dish is based directly upon a novel, which in turn derives its theme from the folktale.

The unusual names of the two girls are intended to indicate the difference in their character. Red is a felicitous color in Japan. Japanese bath tubs are deep and narrow; when not in use they are generally covered with a lid, thus providing an ideal hiding place. Kakezara's poem, aside from its mundane treatment of the subject, observed none of the rigid rules of meter required by traditional poetic styles. Benizara's poem followed the 5-7-5-7-7 syllable arrangement of the Waka or Tanka poetic form. The original text with line-by-line translation follows:

Bon zara ya	Tray, plate, oh!
sara chuu yami ni	plate on mountain over
yuki furite	snow falls
yuki o ne toshite	snow as root using
sodatsu matsu ka na.	growing pine it seems.

• Long ago in a certain place there were two sisters. One was named Benizara, 'Crimson Dish' and the other Kakezara, 'Broken Dish.' Benizara was a former wife's child, while Kakezara was the stepmother's child. Benizara was a very honest and gentle girl, but her stepmother was very cruel to her.

One day she sent the two girls out to gather chestnuts. She gave Benizara a bag with a hole in the bottom, but she gave Kakezara a good one. "You must not come back until you have each filled your bag," she said.

The two set off for the mountains and began to pick up chestnuts. Before long Kakezara's bag was full, and she returned home, leaving Benizara alone. Benizara was an honest girl, and so she worked as hard as she could picking up chestnuts until it began to get dark. It got darker and darker, and she thought she heard a rustling sound, *gasa gasa,* as though a wolf were coming toward her. She suddenly realized how dangerous it was and ran off without even looking where she was going. In the meantime it had become very dark, and she was completely lost. She was filled with despair, but she knew that it would do no good to cry; so she kept on walking, thinking that perhaps she might find a house. Suddenly just ahead she saw a light. She went to where it was and found an old woman alone spinning thread. Benizara explained that she had gone to gather chestnuts but that it was late and she couldn't return home; then she asked if she might please stay overnight there.

The old woman said: "I would like to let you stay here, but both my sons are *oni*. They will soon be coming home and would eat up anyone they found here. Instead, I will tell you how to find your way home." And she carefully explained which road to take. Then she filled her bag with chestnuts and gave her a little box and a handful of rice. "Take the chestnuts to your mother. This little box is a magic box; if there is ever anything that you need, just say what you would like, then tap on the box three times and what you want will appear. Now if you meet my *oni* sons on your way home, chew some of the rice and spread it around your mouth; then lie down and pretend that you are dead."

Benizara thanked her for everything and started for home on the road she had been told to take. After a while she heard the sound of a flute coming toward her. She chewed some of the rice and spread it around her mouth, then lay down by the side of the road and pretended that she was dead. Soon a red *oni* and a blue *oni* came along. "Hey, older brother, I smell human beings," said one and went over to the side of the road to look. "It's no good, older brother, she's already rotten. Her mouth is full of worms," he said. And they went on down the road blowing their flutes.

Benizara listened to the sound of the flutes growing fainter and fainter in the distance; then she continued on down the road that she had been told to take.

Soon morning came. At home her stepmother was thinking to herself that during the night the wolves would have surely eaten Benizara, when just then the girl arrived home. Far from being dead, she had a whole bag full of chestnuts; so the stepmother had nothing to scold her about. ↙ *more similar to "cinderella"*

One day some time after this a play was to be given in the village. The stepmother took Kakezara and went to see it, giving Benizara a great deal of work which had to be done before they returned home. Benizara was working as hard as she could, when some of her friends came and asked her to go with them to see the play. Benizara said that her stepmother had given her so much work to do that she could not go, but her friends said, "We will help you and then you can go," and so, all working together, they soon finished a whole day's work.

Her friends were all wearing beautiful kimonos, but Benizara had nothing but rags to wear. She wondered what she should do; then she thought about the little box she had received from the old woman in the mountains. She took it out and said that she would like to have a kimono. She was given a beautiful kimono. She put it on and went to see the play. When she got there, Kakezara was begging her mother for some candies and Benizara threw her some. When she did this, a nobleman who had come to see the performance of the play saw what happened. *magic* *lucky accident*

The next day the nobleman's colorful procession came to the village. The lord's palanquin stopped in front of Benizara's house. Kakezara's mother was overjoyed and dressed Kakezara in her very best to meet him. The lord got out of the palanquin and said, "There should be two girls here; bring out the other one too."

The stepmother had put Benizara in the bath tub to hide her, but there was nothing she could do but obey the lord's command, and so she brought her out. In comparison to Kakezara, Benizara looked very shabby, but the lord said, "Which one of these two came to see the performance of the play yesterday?"

"It was this one, Kakezara."

"No, it wasn't that one," said the lord, but the mother kept insisting that it was. Finally it was decided to ask each of them to compose a song. The lord took a plate and put it on a tray; then he piled some salt in the plate and stuck a pine needle in it. He commanded that they each compose a poem, using that as a subject.

In a loud voice Kakezara sang,

> Put a plate on a tray,
> Put some salt on the plate,
> Stick a pine needle in the salt;
> It'll soon fall over.

Then she hit the lord on the head and ran off. Next Benizara sang,

> A tray and plate, oh!
> A mountain rises from the plate,
> On it, snow has fallen.
> Rooted deep into the snow,
> A lonely pine tree grows.

When he heard this song, the lord praised it very highly. Preparations were soon made, and Benizara was put into a beautiful palanquin; then she rode off to the lord's palace.

Kakezara's mother watched in silence; then she put Kakezara in a huge empty basket, saying, "Now, Kakezara, you too may go to the lord's palace." She dragged her along, but she did it so violently that Kakezara tumbled over the edge of a deep ditch and fell to her death.

• 39 • The Salt-Grinding Millstones

Type 565, The Magic Mill. Kata No. 173, "The Salt-Grinding Millstones." Collected in Tsuchibuchi-mura, Kamihei-gun, Iwate-ken, from Tanie Haneishi.

Thompson, p. 72, cites the intensive study of Antti Aarne, who concluded that The Magic Mill *was a special development of the widespread tale involving three stolen magic objects,* The Table, the Ass, and the Stick. *This parent tale appears in a collection of sixth-century Chinese Buddhist legends and is well known at present in India. The explanation as to why the sea is salt Aarne believed to come from an old sailor's tradition.*

The tale of The Table, the Ass, and the Stick *does not appear in Japan. The tale of the stolen mill, on the other hand, while widely told in Europe, also appears in Japanese oral tradition in fourteen versions but has not been reported at all in India and only once in China.*

Aarne did not have access to Japanese versions of the salt mill tale; a re-study of the whole tale complex is needed to elucidate the relationship of the European and Asiatic traditions.

Families without a male heir often adopt a husband for the oldest daughter. The adopted husband takes his wife's last name and often assumes a subservient role in his wife's family. Few men are willing to enter into such an arrangement except for a definite economic advantage. A familiar proverb says, "As long as you have even a single coin, never become an adopted husband."

Since prosperity in the new year was felt to depend on a family's having at least sufficient food to offer the gods and to prepare for the last meal of the old year, the year's end meal was of particular significance. In addition to rice, numerous special dishes were generally prepared.

• In a certain place there were two brothers. The older brother was a very unpleasant fellow, but the younger brother was very good and intelligent.

The older brother wanted to marry his younger brother off as an adopted husband as soon as possible so that he would not have to worry about him, but the younger brother wanted to remain single and had no desire to go somewhere and become an adopted husband.

After a while, however, he did take a wife. They borrowed a hut from someone and lived in it. When winter came there was less work than he had expected, and they were in distress. Then the last day of the year came, and he went to his older brother's house to borrow one *sho* [about one half gallon] of rice. His older brother said, "What is this! Is there anyone stupid enough to have no rice to eat at the year's end feast? After all it comes but once a year! And even worse than that, you have gone and gotten married. You can go somewhere else and tell your story." And he completely refused to give him anything. Without a word, the younger brother left his older brother's house.

He was crossing the mountain when he met an old man with a long beard who was picking up firewood. "Where are you going?" asked the old man.

"Tonight is the last night of the year, but we have no rice to offer to the Toshigami [literally, year deity], and so I am just walking about, going nowhere in particular," replied the young man.

"Well, that is too bad. Here, I will give you this, you may take it with you," and he gave him a tiny *manju* [steamed dumpling] made from wheat flour. Then he added, "Take this *manju* and go over there to the temple of the deity of the forest. Behind the temple there is a hole in the ground. There are some *kobito* [literally, little people] who live in that hole; they will ask you to give them the *manju*, but you must tell them that you will not exchange it for money or anything but a pair of millstones. The *kobito* dearly love *manju*."

The young man thanked the old man and went to the temple in the middle of the forest as he had been told. He looked behind the temple and saw that, sure enough, there was a hole there. He went down into the hole and found a large number of *kobito*, who were making a great deal of noise. He wondered what they were doing; when he looked closely, he could see that they were trying to climb up a reed stalk but were falling off and trying again, then falling off and trying again. He thought this very strange and said, "Here, I'll help you," and picking them up, he soon had put them where they were trying to go. The *kobito* were very happy and said in awe, "Oh, what a huge man you are; you are really strong!" Just then they noticed the wheat flour *manju* that he was carrying. "Oh, oh, what a nice looking thing that is you're carrying; how unusual it looks! Please let us have it, will you?" And they spread out some gold in front of him.

As the younger brother had been instructed by the old man, he said, "No, I don't want gold. I will trade this for your mill-stones." The *kobito* were troubled. "There are no other mill-stones in the world like these; they are our treasure. But there is nothing else to do; we will trade them to you." And so they handed them over to him.

The young man gave the *kobito* the *manju*, and taking the tiny millstones, he climbed out of the hole. Just as he got outside, he heard a voice as small as a mosquito's calling, "You're killing me, you're killing me!" He looked around carefully and found that one of the *kobito* was caught between the supports of his high clogs. He carefully took him out and put him back in the hole.

He set off again and came to where the old man had been on the mountain pass. The old man was there again. He said, "Oh, did you get the millstones? If you turn those millstones to the right, anything you want will come out. If you turn them to the left, they will stop."

The younger brother happily returned home. When he got home, his wife had grown very tired of waiting. "Today is the celebration of the last day of the year, and where have you been?" she complained. "Did you go over to your brother's place and get something to eat?"

"It's all right. Hurry, spread out a straw mat here," he said. His wife spread out a mat, and he put the millstones on it. "Make rice, make rice," he said, turning the stones. Rice came pouring out in a stream, *zoko zoko,* one *to* [about four gallons], then two *to*. Next he said, "Make salmon," and two salted salmon, then three, came sliding out, *hyoko hyoko*. After everything necessary for their feast had been provided by the millstones, they had a very happy year's end feast; then they went to sleep.

The next morning was New Year's Day. The young man said, "Since we are now so rich, it is no fun living in a little hut like this; make us a new house." And he turned the millstones. A splendid mansion appeared. Then he made many storehouses, a long house for servants, a horse barn, and seven horses, all from the millstones.

"Make *mochi*. Make *sake*," he said, turning the millstones, and *mochi* and *sake* appeared. He invited all his relatives in the neighborhood and made a great celebration. The villagers were very surprised, and all came to the feast. His older brother was astounded. He thought it so strange that he could not restrain himself but went around here and there, all about the house, trying to see how it had been done.

The younger brother thought that he would make some cakes and candies to give the villagers as presents, so he went to the next room and said, "Make sweetmeats, make sweetmeats," and turned the millstones. While he was doing this, the older brother peeked in and saw what he was doing. "Ah ha, now I see, it is all done by those millstones," he said.

When the feast was over, the villagers all returned home. The younger brother and his wife went to bed. After they had gone to sleep, the older brother crept silently into the next room and stole the millstones, then fled. He also took some *mochi* and some sweetmeats. Taking everything he had gotten, he ran until he came to the seashore. Luckily there was a boat tied up there. He jumped in and pushed off. He decided that he would take the millstones to some place where he could become a very rich man. He began to row the boat with all his might and rowed a good way out to sea, when he began to get hungry. He ate the *mochi* and the sweet cakes and candies, but with so much sweet stuff, he felt hungry for salt. There was none in the boat so he decided that this would be a good chance to try the millstones. He said, "Well, well, make some salt, make some salt," and he turned the millstones. Immediately, salt began to pour, *doshi doshi,* from the stones. He soon thought that he had enough, but he did not know how to make the stones stop. He became frightened, but the stones kept on turning and making salt until the boat was full; then finally it sank, and he sank with it, down into the sea.

Since there was no one to turn the millstones toward the left, they are still at the bottom of the sea, turning and turning, *guru guru,* and making salt, and that is why the sea water is so salty.

·40· *The Magic Ear*

Type 671, The Three Languages. Kata No. 171A, "The Listening Hood." Collected in Naze City, Oshima-gun, Kagoshima-ken, from Tetsuya Fujii.

Power to know animal speech is an old and widespread theme in folklore. Thompson, p. 83, notes that Siegfried in Norse myth and Melampus in Greek mythology possessed the power of understanding the language of animals. Tales containing the motif have appeared in ancient Indian collections, including the Ramayana *and the* Jataka, *and are still popular in oral tradition in that country. Fourteen versions of the tale given here have been recorded in Japan.*

• ONCE THERE was a young man who was walking along the beach. He came to a shoal and saw a little sea bream that had been chased by a bigger fish into the shallow water where it was flopping helplessly about. "Hey, little fish, if you get into such a shallow place, some hungry person is sure to come along and catch you and eat you. Here, I'll put you back into deep water. You'd better go back to your island as fast as you can."

The young man put the little sea bream back into deep water and went on his way, happy that he had been able to do a good deed that day. As he walked along, he heard a voice behind him calling, "Hallo! Please wait a moment." He turned around and saw a young lady so beautiful that he thought she must be a goddess. Since he had never seen her before, he thought that she had surely mistaken him for someone else, so he continued on his way. The young lady called again, "Please wait a moment," and this time he stopped and asked, "Is it me that you are calling?"

"Yes," she replied, "I am a messenger from the king of Neriya. You have saved the life of his only daughter, and I've been sent to escort you down to his kingdom in the sea. Please come with me."

"I can't swim," said the young man, "and so I cannot go to Neriya."

"Oh, you need not worry about that," said the young lady; "I am actually a jellyfish, and so all you need to do is climb on my back, and I shall take you there."

The two of them went to the edge of the water, and the lady turned into a large jellyfish. He climbed on her back, and as they were descending to the dragon palace, the jellyfish said to him, "When the dragon king asks you if there is anything you would like to have as a present, you should reply that there is nothing particular that you would like except the magic ear which is displayed in an alcove. If you ask for this, even though it is the only one of its kind in the whole kingdom, you will be sure to receive it since you have saved the life of the king's only daughter."

When they arrived in Neriya, the young man was given a great feast with dancing. It is said that even an octopus with a towel wrapped around its head performed a dance, but I don't remember exactly about that.

The young man stayed quite a while and was very well taken care of. When it came time for him to return, the king of Neriya said to him, "I will give you whatever you wish; please tell me what you would like to have."

"There is nothing I would like to have except the magic ear which is displayed in the alcove," replied the young man.

"In all of Neriya," said the king, "there is only one treasure like that, but I shall give it to you since you have saved my daughter's life," and he took the magic ear and gave it to the young man.

After he had been given the magic ear, the young man again mounted the jellyfish and was returned to his home; then the jellyfish parted from him, and he was left sitting alone on the beach.

As he sat there, he saw some sparrows going *chuu chuu,* chirp, chirp. He decided to try out the magic ear. He put it to his ear and was surprised to find that he could understand what the sparrows were saying. He listened closely and heard: "Human beings are supposed to be so smart, but really they know nothing. There in the middle of the little river which is flowing by this very tree, the rock that people use as a stepping-stone is solid gold, and they don't know it," and the sparrows laughed among themselves.

The young man thought this the strangest thing he'd ever heard. He went to the river and saw that sure enough, there was the rock the sparrows were talking about. He picked it up and washed the moss off it and found that it was a glittering lump of gold, just as the sparrows had said.

He put the lump of gold into his purse and was walking along thinking how lucky he had been when he heard a couple of crows going ḳaa ḳaa, caw, caw, in the top of a pine tree. He again put the magic ear up to his ear and heard: "Human beings are nothing but fools"—so the crows were saying. "They have called all the famous doctors there are, but none of them can heal the nobleman's daughter. The girl's disease is not one to be healed by medicines. When the roof of the nobleman's house was being thatched, a snake was put in with the thatching grass by mistake. If someone would only get the snake out and give it something to eat, the girl would immediately get well again."

The young man, thinking that that was a good thing to have heard, went to the nobleman's house. Outside the gate he saw a signboard on which was written, "If anyone can heal my only daughter, he shall be given anything he desires as a reward."

The young man entered the house and announced, "I have come to cure the girl's disease."

All the doctors there laughed, and said, "Even we have not been able to cure her, and this dirty, ragged young man comes and thinks that he can!"

But the nobleman, since the girl was his only daughter, was so anxious to have her healed that he was willing to try anything and commanded that the young man be allowed to try.

The young man went into the girl's room and looked at her. "This disease is a curse brought by some animal having been mistreated. There must be a snake buried in the roof thatching," he said, repeating what he had heard the crows say.

The nobleman called his retainers and commanded them to

tear off the roof thatching immediately. They began digging in the thatching and soon found the snake, just as the young man had said. It was nearly dead from hunger and in great agony. They rushed to give it some rice. It ate the rice and, regaining some of its strength, crawled for a distance of only one *shaku* [about one foot]. Just as it did this, the sick girl sat up in her bed.

The snake was given some more rice, and this time crawled about two *shaku*. When it did this, the girl could stand up. After this the snake completely regained its strength and, *suru suru,* went gliding off somewhere and disappeared; and the girl was completely healed of her disease. The young man later became her husband.

•41• *The* Choja *Who Became a Monkey*

Type 750B, Hospitality Rewarded. Kata No. 244, "The Rich Man Who Became a Monkey." Collected on Okierabu Island, Oshima-gun, Kagoshima-ken, from Kubomori Sashi.

Thompson, p. 135, comments that the eminent Swedish folklorist, Carl von Sydow, has traced European versions of this tale back to an eighth-century legend of St. Germanus. It also appears in connection with the god Thor in Scandinavian mythology.

A Japanese variant of the tale is incorporated into a well-known Noh drama, Hachi-no-Ki ("The Potted Tree"), laid in the Kamakura period of the eleventh and twelfth centuries. Twenty-nine texts have been collected in Japan.

• THERE WAS once a *choja* named Agari, who lived in a great mansion. Nearby a *choja* named Iri lived alone with his wife. They were extremely poor; they had no children and no money.

One time as the year was drawing to a close and December 29 had come, the old man said to his wife, "Wouldn't it be a good idea to go over to Agari *choja*'s house and borrow some rice and *miso* to eat for the year-end feast."

"You will only waste your breath trying to borrow anything

from Agari *choja*," said his wife. "We have a tiny bit of millet seed left; I can make some gruel with it and that will be our feast for the year-end celebration."

Now just at that time, the Sun deity came down from the sky to see what was in men's hearts. He took the form of a poor young itinerant priest going about begging for his food and a place to sleep. First he went to the house of Agari *choja*.

"Truly, I have no right to make a request like this, but I have nowhere to stay tonight. May I please spend the night here," he begged.

"What, don't you know it is December 29, and nearly the end of the year? Why, if you keep bothering me like this, I'll break every bone in your body," and Agari *choja* refused to give him anything.

"If that is your wish, then it is all right," said the traveling priest, and this time he went to the house of the old man named Iri.

"Grandfather, grandmother," he called out, "it is I, a traveling priest. Here at the end of the year, could you give me a place to stay for the night."

"Yes, yes, hurry and come in. We have nothing to give you to eat, only some thin millet gruel, but you're welcome to some of that." And the old man and his wife gladly welcomed the priest into their house.

The traveling priest said to the old woman, "Take a one *sho* [about one-half gallon] kettle and wash it, then put in three green leaves, fill it with water, and set it on the fire."

The old woman did as she was told. Immediately, the kettle was filled with pickles and relishes.

"This time take the rice kettle and wash it well," the priest said. The old woman did so; from his purse the priest took three grains of rice, dropped them into the pot, and said, "Now set this on the fire and boil it." The old woman did so and, when it was done, found that the kettle was full of delicious white rice. The three of them sat down to the feast and so had a happy year-end celebration.

After they had finished eating, the priest said, "Grandfather and grandmother, you are very poor and have now become quite old. Would you like to receive some great treasure, or would you rather be young again, as you once were?"

"We would rather return to our youth and be seventeen or eighteen years old again," they replied.

"Then take your great iron kettle and fill it with hot water," the priest commanded. After they had done so, he took some yellow powder from his purse and sprinkled it on the water. "Now," he said, "you must both get into the water at the same time, not one before the other." The old man and his wife got into the water together, and when they did so, they became young people of seventeen or eighteen.

In the meantime morning came, and the priest said, "You must take some water and throw it on the fire so that it goes out. Then, grandmother, you must go to Agari *choja*'s house and borrow some coals to start the fire again."

The grandmother went to Agari *choja*'s house and asked for some coals. Everyone was greatly surprised to see that the old lady had become young again, and when she told them how the traveling priest had come and they had received their youth again, Agari *choja* cried, "What a foolish thing I've done! If I had let him stay here, we could have been the ones to have received this good fortune. Please ask him what we can do to get him to come and stay here."

The grandmother returned home. When she told what had happened, the traveling priest soon went over to Agari *choja*'s house. "You are very wealthy," he said to Agari *choja*. "There is nothing you lack; what more could you want?"

"Because I have much money, I keep wanting more," he replied. "Please give me some more."

"You really have no need of more money," said the priest, "but I can make you young again." He had them fill the bath and heat it. He took out his purse, and this time he put in some red powder. "Now you must all get in the bath together," he commanded. The whole family got in the bath, but when they did so, the *choja* and his wife became monkeys; the children became dogs; the menservants, cats; the maidservants, mice; and one manservant even became a goat.

Then the priest returned to the house of the poor man and

his wife and told them that they could now have the whole estate of Agari *choja*.

They went to live in the rich man's mansion, but every evening two monkeys would come and bother them so much that they could hardly bear it. They had nearly decided to return to their former hut when the traveling priest came by again.

They told him how they were being troubled, and the priest said, "You must take two black stones, heat them, and put them where the monkeys always come to sit down." They did as they were told, and when the monkeys came that evening, they sat on the hot stones and were severely burned.

After that the monkeys never returned. It is said that the fact that monkeys have red spots on their buttocks is because the two were badly burned that time. The old man and his wife who had been made young again are said to be still living comfortably in the *choja*'s mansion.

·42· *The Skeleton's Song*

Motifs N271, "Murder will out," and E632.1, "Speaking bones of murdered person reveal murder," are central. This tale is also related to Type 780, The Singing Bone. Kata No. 223, "The Skeleton's Song." Collected in Tsuchibuchi-mura, Kamihei-gun, Iwate-ken, from Tanie Haneishi.

Twelve versions of this tale have been recorded in Japan, where it enters the cycle of stories of wise judgments attributed to a famous seventeenth-century Japanese judge, Ooka Echizen-no-Kami.

The tale is found all over the world. Ikeda, p. 215, notes that literary versions appear in sixteenth-century Chinese works. The German folklorist, Lutz Mackenson, made an exhaustive study of the tale, but no Japanese versions were available to him. He did use twelve variants from Africa. Dorson, in Negro Folktales in Michigan, *pp. 62–63, "Talking Bones," records a variant similar to some of the African versions used by Mackenson in his study.*

• LONG AGO there were two good friends named Kami Shichibe and Shimo Shichibe. They decided to go to another country and find work, and so they set off. Shimo Shichibe worked very hard and earned a great deal of money, but Kami Shichibe fell in with a bunch of bad companions and did nothing but waste his time in evil pleasures.

In this way the days and months passed until three years were gone, and Shimo Shichibe decided to return to his home country. He asked Kami Shichibe if he wanted to return, too, and he replied, "I want very much to return, but I have no clothes to wear."

Now since the two of them had left their home village together, Shimo Shichibe did not want to leave Kami Shichibe and go home alone. He gave him clothes and traveling money so that they could return together; then the two of them set out. However, when they got to the mountain pass which marked the border of their home country, Kami Shichibe attacked Shimo Shichibe and killed him. He took his money and, pretending that nothing had happened, returned to his home village.

When he got home he told all the villagers: "Shimo Shichibe changed into a completely different person after he left the village and went to another country. He did nothing but evil, so he had no money for traveling expenses and could not return home."

Soon after this Kami Shichibe began to gamble and play dice. In a short while he had lost all the money he had taken from Shimo Shichibe. He could no longer stay in the village, so he set off for another country. On his way he passed through the mountain pass where he had killed Shimo Shichibe. As he was going through the pass, he heard a voice calling, "Shichibe, Shichibe." Wondering who it was, he turned around and looked, but there was no one there. Thinking that he had only imagined that he had heard something, he started off again, but the voice came again, "Shichibe, Shichibe."

"Well, this is surely something strange," he thought and, listening carefully, found that the voice was coming from a thicket by the side of the road.

Wondering what strange thing it was, Kami Shichibe peeked into the thicket and saw a skeleton there; its white teeth were turned toward him, and it was laughing loudly. While Kami Shichibe looked on in surprise, the skeleton said: "Well, my friend, it's been a long time. Have you forgotten me? I am Shimo Shichibe, whom you killed and robbed here three years ago. I kept thinking that I might meet you again sometime and have been waiting here day after day for you to come. Today my wish has been fulfilled, and I have the chance to see you again. I have never been so happy before."

Kami Shichibe was very much surprised and tried to run away, but the skeleton seized the skirt of his kimono in its bony hand and would not let go.

"Where are you going now?" asked the skeleton. Kami Shichibe had no choice but to tell the truth. "I went home to the village but the money soon disappeared, and so I set out on a trip to look for work, and here I am. I want to hurry on now, so please let me go."

"Really? Well, I see that you haven't changed; you are always in trouble. Now how about my doing dances for you? Why don't you take me along with you? You can put me in a box and carry me with you. I won't need anything to eat or anything to wear. There is no other job like this where you can earn so much with so little expense. You are probably wondering what sort of dances I can do. Well, I'll show you right away; please watch me awhile," and the skeleton began to dance. Rattling and banging his bones together, waving his arms, and lifting his legs, he performed various dances.

"Well, Shichibe, that's how I do it. If you sing and call the tune, I can dance any kind of dance you want. What do you say; we could make a lot of money, couldn't we?"

Kami Shichibe agreed that it would be a good way to make a lot of money, and so he took the skeleton as it had requested and continued on his journey.

Reports of Kami Shichibe and his dancing skeleton spread from town to village, and even the lord of the country heard of it. Kami Shichibe was called to the lord's castle, and there he was told to make the skeleton dance in the great reception room of the castle. However, for some reason, the skeleton would not do a single dance before the lord. Kami Shichibe turned blue, then red; he sang various songs, called various tunes, played various accompaniments, but the skeleton would not dance a step.

Becoming angry, Kami Shichibe took his whip and began to beat the skeleton. It then got up and went before the lord. "My lord, I have been performing dances about the country just so that I could come into your presence. This fellow killed me and robbed me of my money at the pass on the border of this country," and the skeleton told everything that had happened.

The lord was very surprised. "There are certainly some things in this world that are very strange," he said, then cried, "Quick, bind that fellow with a rope and take him to be tried!" Kami Shichibe was taken and tried. He confessed to all his sins; then he was crucified.

Part V
Good Fortune

·43· The Charcoal Burner Choja

Motifs T125, "Lazy boy and industrious girl matched," and D475.1.1, "Transformation: coals to gold," are the principal motifs here. Kata No. 183B, "The Charcoal Burner Choja." The tale is assigned by Ikeda to Type 822, The Lazy Boy and the Industrious Girl, but is similar to the form found in Renaissance jestbooks and medieval exempla only in one element, the matching of a man and woman of opposite character. Collected on Okierabu Island, Oshima-gun, Kagoshima-ken, by Kubomori Sashi.

There are twenty-nine variants recorded in Japan. Dorson, in Folk Legends of Japan, pp. 179–82, gives a version of this tale as a legend explaining the origin of a shrine.

A fate of one-half gallon of salt indicates that the girl would become so wealthy that her household would use that amount of salt every day. A fate of one stick of bamboo indicates that the man would be so poor that his possessions would not exceed the value of a piece of bamboo.

Most Japanese farmers harvest at least two crops a year, since barley and wheat ripen in the spring. Barley is a secondary food and is usually eaten only if the supply of rice is insufficient. After the initial pounding, only the best part of the grain was selected for further grinding, and from that, the best part was again taken out and ground still finer.

The various parts of the house and its outbuildings were all thought to be animated with an appropriate kami. Carelessness or lack of respect could drive these deities away.

Parched rice tea is used by poverty-stricken peasants as a substitute for green tea, just as European peasants use parched wheat or barley for coffee.

• ONCE THERE were two *choja*, one named Agari, 'Sunrise,' and one named Iri, 'Sunset.' They were fishing companions and would go along the beach together every evening.

After some time it happened that both their wives became pregnant. One evening the two men went down to the beach together as usual; but since the tide had not yet gone out, they decided to rest while waiting for it, and so, taking a piece of driftwood as a pillow, they lay down to sleep. Agari *choja* soon went to sleep. While Iri *choja* was still awake, the deity of Nira [the dragon kingdom of the sea] came and said to the piece of driftwood which the two were using as a pillow, "Driftwood, driftwood, Agari *choja* and Iri *choja* have just had children born; let's go and bestow their fates upon them."

The driftwood answered: "I am now being used as a pillow by these men, and so I cannot go. Please go in my stead and give the children their fate."

The deity of Nira went and bestowed the children's fate upon them and soon returned. "I have assigned their station in life. Agari *choja*'s child is a girl; she shall have a fate of one *sho* [about one-half gallon] of salt. Iri *choja*'s child was a boy; to him I have assigned a fate of one stick of bamboo."

"One *sho* of salt is too much, isn't it," said the driftwood.

"No, the girl was born to at least that much," said the deity of Nira, and so he departed.

Iri *choja* had listened to the deities' conversation, and after hearing that his own child had been given a fate of one stick of bamboo, he felt that he would have to think of something to remedy that as soon as possible, and so he woke the sleeping Agari *choja*.

"Agari-*danna*, Agari-*danna*, I have just had a dream. I dreamed that both your wife and mine had children. Let's go home right away and see." And so the two of them left off fishing and returned home.

On the way home Iri *choja* said, "Agari-*danna*, let us discuss this matter. If my child is a girl and your child is a boy, let us agree that I shall receive him as my son-in-law. Then again, if your child is a girl and my child is a boy, I will give him to you as a son-in-law."

Agari *choja* thought this was satisfactory, and so they made an agreement and returned home. They found that at Agari *choja*'s house a girl had been born and at Iri *choja*'s place a boy had been born.

The two children were raised with care. When they reached

the age of eighteen, Agari *choja* said to Iri *choja,* "Since it was an agreement that we made on the night that they were born, please give me your son as my son-in-law," and so he received Iri *choja's* son as his son-in-law.

The two young people were married and began their life together. The day of the May barley harvest festival came, and the wife prepared a dish of food made from barley, which she offered to the deities and to the ancestors. Then she gave some to her husband saying, "This is a dish made from one *hyo* [about two bushels] of barley which has been pounded until it became one *to* [about four gallons] and that pounded until it became one *sho* [about one-half gallon]. Since today is the festival of the new barley harvest, wouldn't you like to eat some of this?"

Her husband, however, became angry and cried, "If it were the hearts of rice, I would eat it, but I have never even eaten raw pounded rice. Are you going to offer me food made from new barley?" and he sent both the tray and the food flying with a kick. When the wife saw this, she said, "I can no longer bear to stay here. My father has given you this house and these storehouses, so do with them as you please. All that I will take is the tray and bowls that you have kicked out. I will go and live somewhere else." She took the tray and bowls, then picked up every grain of the spilled food and left the house.

When she left the gate, it was raining. Two storehouse deities were standing there in the rain talking. "It has come to the point where even valuable barley is being kicked around. If we stay here in this house we too will certainly be kicked about by that One-Stick-of-Bamboo fellow. The charcoal burner, Goro, who lives on the plains of Ushinichi is of good character and is also a handsome fellow. Let us go there, shall we?"

The wife heard the deities' conversation and said to herself, "That's a good thing to hear. Since our own storehouse deities have talked about him, I will go and try to find the house of Goro, the charcoal burner." She set off and walked and walked until the evening of the next day. Finally, far in the distance, she could see a tiny light flickering on and off. She continued on toward the light and came to the hut of Goro, the charcoal burner.

"Excuse me, please. Excuse me, please," called the woman.

"Yes," answered Goro and came to the door.

"Would you please let me stay here for just one night?" she asked.

"I have such a tiny hut that if you get your head in, your feet stick out, and if you get your feet in, your head sticks out. How could I ever let such a beautiful person as you take lodging here? If you go on a little farther, there is a large house. Why don't you go there and get a place to stay?"

"A woman cannot keep on walking when it is dark like this; please let me stay even if only under the eaves of the house," begged the woman again and again.

"Well, all right then; please come in," and so she was allowed to stay.

When the woman came in, she was given tea made from parched rice. She received the tea; then taking out the barley cakes she had brought with her, she divided them with Goro, and so they ate them. Then the woman said, "Won't you please take me as your wife?"

Goro was very surprised. "Why, if a person like me were to take a beautiful woman such as you for a wife, he would be punished."

"No, nothing like that will happen. Since it is my request, please take me as your wife."

"Since you beg it of me, you may become my wife," agreed Goro.

On the morning of the next day, the woman said to Goro, "Let us go around and look into every charcoal oven that you have, from the very first one that you fired until the last one that you have fired today, every one of them without exception." So the two of them went around and looked into all the ovens, and in each one of them there was pure gold. They took out the gold and had a carpenter make a box for it. In a short time they became very wealthy.

The man whose fate was one stick of bamboo had gradually become poorer and poorer, until finally he had to go from village to village selling things made from bamboo. One day he happened to come to the house of Goro, the charcoal burner. Goro's wife still remembered the man's face, and she gave him two *sho* [about one gallon] of rice for things which were worth only one *sho,* and for things which were worth two *sho,* she gave him four *sho.*

"What a foolish woman," thought One-Stick-of-Bamboo. "Next time I shall make a huge basket of things and sell them to her."

He made up a huge basket, then returned to Goro's place. The woman took the tray and dishes that she had received when she had parted from him and showed them to the man. When he saw them, he was so ashamed that he went out beneath the tall storehouse and cut out his tongue and died.

The woman dug a grave beneath the storehouse. "I will have nothing to offer on your grave, except that during the May barley harvest festival, I shall place some barley here. You must not ask to eat anything else but that. Also you must guard the storehouse so that animals do not get into it."

Since that time, at the dedication of a new storehouse, it has been the custom to give a woman a small bag of grain which she must be the first to carry into the storehouse.

·44· *Luck from Heaven and Luck from the Earth*

Type 834A, The Pot of Gold and the Pot of Scorpions. Kata No. 207, "Luck from Heaven and Luck from the Earth." Collected in Mitsuke-mura, Minami Kanbara-gun, Niigata-ken, from Motozo Yoshii.

Twenty versions of this tale have been collected in Japan. Eberhard, pp. 229–30, lists seven variants from China; Thompson and Roberts, pp. 101–2, list eight in India. The tale occasionally appears in eastern Europe but seems to be most at home in the Orient.

Since the first dream of the new year is believed to have par-

ticular bearing on one's fortunes throughout the year, it is important that the dream be auspicious.

• LONG, LONG ago an honest old man and an evil old man lived as neighbors.

One time, just as the year was drawing to a close, they happened to meet on the road, and the honest old man said, "When the new year comes, let us each try to have a dream which will come true." The other old man readily consented. They agreed to meet again to tell one another their dreams, then went home.

On the third day of the new year, the honest old man and the evil old man again met on the road. "Did you have a dream last night," asked the evil old man.

"Yes, I did," replied the honest old man.

"I had a very strange dream," said the other.

"I dreamed that luck came to me from heaven," said the honest old man.

"I dreamed that luck came to me from the earth," said the evil old man.

"Well, they were both good dreams," they said and returned home.

Several days after this, the honest old man said to himself, "Today the weather is so warm that I think I will make a third planting of beans," and he went out to prepare the field. As he was digging up the ground, his hoe made a clanging sound as though it had hit a stone. "This is strange," he said; "there shouldn't be any stones here." He dug the stone out and saw that a jar was buried beneath it. "Ah, I've found a jar," he said. He lifted the lid and was much surprised to see that it was full of glittering *oban* and *koban* coins. "This surely must be the lucky thing which the neighboring old man dreamed that he was to receive from the earth. I must hurry over and tell him," and stopping his work, he went over to his neighbor's house.

"Grandfather, I've found the lucky thing that you were to receive from the earth, hurry and get it." He told him how to find it, then returned home.

When he got home, he told his wife what he had done. "The neighboring old man was very happy to hear about what I found," he said. "He has probably already dug up the money and carried it home by now."

"You did a very honorable thing to tell him about it," said his wife. "Come, let's sit by the fireplace where it's warm." So they sat by the fireplace and talked for a while.

The evil old man joyfully hurried out to the field where the jar was buried. Sure enough there was the place where the earth had been dug up, and he soon found the buried jar. "This jar is full of *oban* and *koban* coins," he thought to himself, and lifting the lid, he looked inside, but instead of *oban* and *koban* coins, it was full of writhing snakes.

"What a contemptible trick that filthy old man has played on me," he cried, blazing into anger. "Well, this time, I'll give him a surprise," and he put the jar on his back and went home.

Taking a ladder from his home, the evil old man went over to his neighbor's house and climbed up on the roof. He looked down through the smoke vent. There he saw the honest old man lying beside the fireplace warming his back.

"There he is; he played a dirty trick on me, and now he's lying there warming his back!" The evil old man got more and more angry and, taking the lid from the jar, poured the contents out upon the head of the old man below. However, instead of snakes, real *oban* and *koban* coins fell everywhere into the room where the old man and his wife were.

"Look, old woman," cried the honest old man, "the neighboring old man received luck from the earth and now we are receiving luck from heaven," and they were filled with rejoicing. And so the dream he had had on the second day of the new year had come true, and they became very, very wealthy.

•45• *The Man Who Bought a Dream*

Type 1645A, Dream of Treasure Bought. *Kata No. 204, "The Man Who Bought a Dream." Collected in Kuzumaki-mura, Minami Kanbara-gun, Niigata-ken, from Etsu Makino.*

Eighteen versions of this tale are recorded in Japanese collec-

tions. It appears as a legend about a choja *named Sanya in Dorson's* Folk Legends of Japan, *pp. 185–86.*

This tale is similar to the legend of King Guntram that is widely known in Europe. This thirteenth-century Frankish king was supposed to have dreamed of crossing an iron bridge and finding buried treasure. As he slept, his servant observed a mouse run from the king's mouth. The servant helped the mouse cross a stream on his sword and watched it disappear into a hole, then return to the king's mouth. When the king awakened, gold was found at the place the mouse had gone.

The tale is particularly well known in Scandinavia, where King Guntram is generally replaced by a pair of laborers or traveling companions. Reidar Th. Christiansen has assigned the story to No. 4000 in his index of Norwegian migratory legends. The only known variant of the tale in the United States was recorded in Maine in the seventeenth century. This version, reported by Horace Beck, p. 37, lacks the dream about treasure but in other respects is strikingly similar to the Japanese tradition.

• LONG AGO in a certain place there lived two merchants. They went out together on a peddling trip. One day as they traveled along, they came to a place similar to the beach at our village of Teradomari; since they were very tired from walking, they decided to stop there and rest.

"Oh, I am so sleepy," said the older of the two.

"If you want to sleep a while, please go ahead," said the other, and soon the older merchant was fast asleep and snoring loudly.

"Why, he's gone to sleep already," said the younger one, and he idly watched his companion as he lay sleeping. Soon he saw a horsefly come from the older man's nose and fly off in the direction of Sado Island. "Now, that was a strange thing," he thought. Soon the horsefly came back and crawled into the sleeping man's nose, where it disappeared from sight.

Shortly after this, the older man awoke. "I had the strangest dream," he said.

"What sort of dream was it," asked his companion.

"Well, I dreamed there was a *choja* who lived on Sado Island. In his garden there was a white camellia tree, full of blossoms.

A horsefly came flying from the root of the tree and told me to dig at that spot. I did so, and there I found a jar full of gold. That is what my dream was."

The young man eagerly listened to the dream, and then he said, "Will you sell me your dream?"

"What!" cried the other. "How can anyone buy a dream?"

"I'll give you anything you want for it, please sell it to me," he begged.

"Well, then, how much will you give me?"

"If you'll sell it, I'll give you three hundred pieces of money" [denomination not specified in text].

The older man agreed, and so the deal was made, and the dream was sold for three hundred pieces of money.

When they finished their journey, the man who had bought the dream returned to his village. He pretended that he was going on another peddling trip, but he secretly crossed over to Sado Island.

Traveling here and there on the island, he searched everywhere until he finally found the house of the *choja*. He went to the *choja*'s mansion, and when the master of the house appeared, he said to him, "I am a poor man who has come over from Echigo province. I am reluctant to ask you; but would it be possible to find employment in your service, even if it is only sweeping the garden?"

"You've come at just the right time," said the *choja*. "I was just thinking of hiring someone to help sweep the garden. If you're willing to work, I will hire you."

And so it came about that the man who had bought the dream was employed in the *choja*'s garden. Every day he worked faithfully, waiting for spring to come.

The cold winter finally came to an end and spring arrived. Gradually the weather became warmer and warmer, and the garden was filled with blooming plants and trees. The camellia trees came into bloom, but for some reason, there were only red flowers; not a single tree had white blossoms.

The young man never gave up hope and patiently waited for the following spring. Spring again came and the flowers in the garden began blooming. Every day the young man went to see

if any white camellias had bloomed. Finally, one morning, there
was one camellia tree covered with white blossoms.

The young man was overjoyed. That night, being careful to
be seen by no one, he arose and, taking a pair of iron brazier
tongs, went to the garden. He poked in the ground at the root
of the camellia tree and heard the tongs strike, *kotsun kotsun*,
clink, clink, against something solid.

He dug at that spot and soon saw what looked like the lid of
a jar. "This is it, this is it," he cried to himself, lifting the lid to
reveal a jar full of glittering gold. The young man took the jar
of gold out and filled up the hole; then he hid the jar of gold
where no one could find it.

Half a year passed. One day the young man went to the master of the house and said: "You have taken good care of me for
a long time, but now I must return to my home and observe the
anniversary of my parents' death. I beg of you, please let me go."

"You have served faithfully for a long time; you may return
now," said the master, giving him some money for his traveling
expenses.

Thanking the master, the man who had bought the dream
took the jar of gold and wrapped it up to look like part of his
baggage; then he returned to the province of Echigo.

He became a very wealthy *choja* and was able to spend the
rest of his life in comfort.

· 46 · The Advice That Cost a Thousand Ryo

*Type 910G, Man Buys a Pennyworth of Wit. Kata No. 320, "The
Precepts Bought for a Thousand Ryo." Collected on Koshiki Island, Satsuma-gun, Kagoshima-ken, from Jiro Ishihara.*

*This tale, according to Thompson, p. 164, originated in the Ori-
ent. He notes that it appears in the older literary collections from
India, in Arabic and Persian reworkings, and in most of the
books of exempla and jests in the Middle Ages and the Renaissance. It has been adopted into oral tradition in most European*

countries as well as in the Near East and India. The tale is well known in Japan, where thirty-six oral versions have been recorded.

The ryo *of feudal periods was sometimes called* yen. *The present unit on which the Japanese monetary system is based is also called the* yen, *but it is of much smaller value than the* yen *or* ryo *of feudal Japan.*

• THERE WERE a man and his wife who were very, very poor, so poor that they could not even pay the imperial taxes. The wife was a very good woman, and the husband said, "I will go up to the capital and find a place to work. I will save my money, and we can pay the taxes. Please work patiently here until I return." He set off for the capital, where he found employment. He made an agreement to work one year for the wage of thirty *yen*.

He worked for one year and received his thirty *yen*. He quit working and began his journey home, but when it became dark at night he could go no farther. Just as he was wondering if there might not be a house where he could spend the night, he happened to see a light. He went up to it and saw that there was an old man there. "Excuse me, please," he called.

"Come in."

"Please, could I spend the night here?"

"Do you like to hear advice? If you don't, I can't let you stay," said the old man.

The two of them sat down together. The old man said, "My advice costs a great deal; is that all right?"

"If the price is right, I will be glad to pay it."

"When it is raining, don't stay in a rock shelter. All right, give me ten *ryo.*"

"Oh, oh, I don't know what to do. I finally earned thirty *yen,* and now if I have to give you ten *yen,* I will have only twenty *yen* left," said the man, but he gave the old man ten *yen*.

The next morning he left the old man's house and was going along when it began raining and blowing so hard that he could neither go further nor turn back. He decided to take shelter from the wind and rain under the edge of a cliff, but then he remembered the old man's words, "When it's raining, don't stay in a rock shelter." Just then, only four or five *ken* [eight to ten yards] away, the rock cliff crumbled into pieces.

The man continued on his way. Evening came and it again became dark. He again saw a light and called, "Excuse me, please." An old man similar to the old man of the previous night came out. "My advice costs money; can you pay?" asked the old man. "Yes, there is nothing else to do. Please let me stay here tonight."

"If you must hurry, go around another way. Don't travel too fast. All right, give me ten *ryo*," said the old man, and the traveler gave him ten *yen*.

The next morning he came to where he could make his trip shorter by taking a boat. "Captain, please take me across, too," he called.

"Hurry, hurry, get on board," called the captain.

The man remembered, "If you must hurry, take another way; don't travel fast," and so he decided to walk slowly. Just then the ship capsized and sank. Happy at his deliverance, the man continued on his way.

Night fell and it was dark again. Just as before, he stayed at an old man's house. This time he was told, "A short temper makes for loss; now give me ten *ryo*."

In this way, the man returned home without a single piece of money. When he got home, he looked in and saw that his wife was drinking *sake* with the priest from the temple. Wondering if he should go in and kill them both, he again remembered the old man's words, "A short temper makes for loss." He went to the front door and called, "Wife, I've returned."

"Just a moment," called his wife and hid the priest in a big jar. The man came into the house and saw the *sake* and the side dishes. "Did you have a guest?" he asked.

"I dreamed about you last night, so I have been waiting for your return."

"What is this jar for?"

"I was making *miso* for the temple."

"I'll carry it over for you." The man took the jar with the priest in it on his back and went to the temple. "Acolyte, give me 500 *ryo* for this jar," said the man, then went off to the toilet. While he was gone, the priest said to the acolyte, "Take 500 *ryo* from my desk and give it to him."

So the man got 500 *yen,* and after that he lived happily with his wife.

Part VI
Cleverness
and Stupidity

Motifs B601.7, "Marriage to monkey," and K891, "Dupe tricked into jumping to his death," are the principal motifs in this tale. Kata No. 135, "The Monkey Bridegroom." Collected in Kurokawa-mura, Aso-gun, Kumamoto-ken, by Sanji Yagi.

This story about an animal bridegroom employs a theme common to many Japanese traditions of this general type. This theme, that the husband is actually an animal and must be killed so that the bride can return to normal society, is relatively rare in European tales. In the Japanese tales the husband is not an enchanted being, and interest centers on the wife's escaping from him rather than disenchanting him.

Of all animal bridegroom tales in Japan, this one about the monkey is the best known. More than one hundred versions have been recorded. Ikeda, p. 131, reports that it is very popular among professional storytellers.

Gobo [burdock] roots are a staple vegetable in rural Japan. Since they are up to three feet long and only about half an inch in diameter, they are difficult to harvest.

Cherry blossoms are rarely cut from the tree; the national pastime of cherry blossom viewing takes place only in the tree's natural setting. There is a well-known proverb, "Only a fool plucks the cherry blossom." The monkey's willingness to pick the cherry blossoms further revealed his stupidity.

The stylized ending of this tale may have originally been a reminder that refreshments were in order since the tale was completed. This ending is used chiefly in southern Japan.

• In a certain place there lived an old man. One day he went out to dig up *gobo* [burdock] roots, but he couldn't dig out a single one. Just as he was wondering what to do, a monkey came along and called out, "Grandfather, grandfather, shall I help you pull up *gobo* roots?"

"Yes, please help me. If you will dig up some roots for me; I'll give you one of my daughters as your wife."

"Will you really do that!" the monkey cried. "Then I shall come to claim her in three days."

The old man, thinking that the monkey surely would never come to claim one of his daughters, agreed to all he said.

While they were talking, the monkey began pulling up *gobo* roots and soon had a large pile of them. "The monkey certainly has pulled up a lot of roots; perhaps he really intends to come for one of my daughters," the old man thought to himself, beginning to get a little worried.

Finally the monkey had pulled up every *gobo* root in the field. "Well," he said to the old man, "I shall surely come for your daughter." Then he scampered off.

The old man thought to himself: "He must really intend to come. Why did I ever tell him that I'd give him one of my daughters? What shall I do? What shall I do? I don't think that any of my girls will agree to become his wife. I must try to persuade one of them." The old man walked sadly home, talking to himself.

When he got home, he called his eldest daughter and, after telling her what had happened, said, "When the monkey comes in three days, will you go to be his bride?"

"What!" she cried. "Who would ever want to become a monkey's wife!" and she refused even to consider it.

The old man then called his second daughter and asked her the same thing.

"Why," she cried, "what a fool you are! Who would ever make a promise like that? I may be older than our youngest sister, but I'm not going to become that monkey's bride. I don't think anyone would do it," and so she refused completely.

"Since the other two have refused," the old man thought to himself, "I don't think that the youngest will agree either. However, I'll have to ask her; there's nothing else to do." He went to his youngest daughter and told her what he had promised and that the monkey would be coming in three days to get his bride. "Your sisters have both refused. Will you please go and be his bride." His face paling, the old man made his request.

The girl thought for a while, then replied, "Yes, father, since you have promised, I will go."

Upon hearing this, the old man was overjoyed, crying, "Really! Will you really go?"

"I will go because of my duty to you," said the girl, "but you must give me three things to take with me."

"What things do you want?" he asked. "I will give you anything you request."

"Please give me a very heavy mortar, together with a heavy maul for pounding rice and one *to* [about 50 pounds] of rice."

"What!" he cried, "is that all you want! If so, you shall have them," and he soon brought them to her.

On the third day the monkey came as he had promised. The youngest daughter said to him: "I am to become your bride, but when we go back to the mountains, we will want to eat rice *mochi,* so let's take this mortar, maul, and bag of rice with us. You can carry it all on your back."

The monkey loaded everything on his back. It was very, very heavy, but since his bride had requested it, he did not want to refuse, and they set off up the mountain, the monkey carrying his heavy load.

It was just the beginning of April, and on both sides of the road the cherry trees were in full bloom. They traveled along until they came to a place where the road went close to the edge of a deep canyon. At the bottom of the canyon there was a river. At this point the branches of the cherry trees fell over into the canyon, making such a beautiful scene that the girl stopped, saying to the monkey, "Oh, such a lovely cherry tree. Won't you please climb up and get me a branch of those cherry blossoms."

Since this too was a request of his bride, the monkey agreed and began to climb up into one of the trees. "Please get some flowers from the topmost branch," the girl cried from below, so the monkey continued to climb higher and higher. "Isn't this about right?" he asked, but the girl urged him higher and higher until he had climbed up to where the branches were very small and weak.

The load on his back was very heavy, and the branch he was on was very small; suddenly it broke, and the monkey fell headlong into the canyon below, landing with a splash, *dossun,* in

the river. As he sank from sight with the heavy mortar on his
back, he sang this song:

> I do not regret my death,
> But oh, how sad for my poor bride.

And he soon disappeared from view.

The girl was very happy and returned to her home.

Naa, mosu mosu, komen dango. "Well, hallo, hallo, rice cakes."

•48• *The Wife's Portrait*

Type 465, The Man Persecuted because of His Beautiful Wife.
Kata No. 189, "The Wife's Portrait." Collected in Gosen-mura,
Naka Kanbara-gun, Niigata-ken, from Teki Honma.

This tale is popular in Japanese oral tradition with thirty-nine
versions on record. The best-known literary reworking of the tale
is the dramatization by Junji Kinoshita, a playwright who has
made extensive use of folk tradition.

Ikeda, p. 139, notes that this tale, or elements of it, have ap-
peared frequently since the eighth century in Japanese literary
collections such as the Nihongi, *the* Ryoi-ki, *and the* Sangoku
Denki. *The tale is common in eastern Europe, India, and China,*
but no thorough study has been made of it; and so the area of
its origin is not clear.

In feudal Japan it was the prerogative of a ruler to take as his
own wife or concubine any woman who struck his fancy, regard-
less of whether or not she were already married.

Young pine trees are used to decorate the gateposts at the
new year. The pine is a symbol of long life and is usually com-
bined with bamboo, also symbolic of longevity.

The stylized ending of this tale is taken from the cry of the
stall holder at the year's end market, "The market is good; every-
thing is selling out." Cf. "donde hare," explained in the glossary.

• VERY, VERY long ago in a certain place there lived a rather
slow-witted man named Gombei. He became thirty, then forty

years old, but there was no one who would become his wife. He lived all alone in a dirty little hut.

One evening a beautiful woman, such as he had never seen before, came to his hut. "Tonight, please let me stay overnight here," she requested. Gombei was very surprised, but he gladly agreed to let her stay.

As night came, the woman said to him, "You are all alone in the world, and so am I; please take me as your wife." Gombei joyfully agreed, and she became his wife.

Gombei was so in love with his new wife that he hardly knew what he was doing. When he would sit down to make straw sandals, he was constantly looking at her, so that sometimes he would make the sandals five or six *shaku* [five or six feet] long, and they would be unfit for anyone to wear. Or when he would start to make straw rain capes, he could not take his eyes off his wife, and the capes would become longer and longer, one or two *jo* [ten to twenty feet], and no one could wear them. Then again, when he would go out to work in the fields, he would begin to wonder if his wife were all right and, after making one furrow, would run home to see her, then return to his work; but he would only get one more furrow made before he would again start thinking about his wife so much that he would have to run home again to see her. In this way he was hardly able to get any work done at all.

Since her husband could not get his work done, the wife went to the village and had an artist paint her portrait. She brought it home and gave it to Gombei, saying, "Here, this is just like me; please take it and hang it on a branch of a mulberry tree near the field. You can look at it as much as you want as you do your work."

Gombei took the picture and hung it near the field, and from then on he would work every day in the field, always looking at the picture. One day, however, a great wind came and, picking up the picture, whirled it high up into the air. Gombei was grief-stricken. Crying bitterly, he returned home to tell his wife what had happened. She comforted him, saying, "Do not worry so about it. I can easily have another painted just like it."

The wind carried the picture about here and there, finally letting it fall in the garden of the lord of the province. When the lord saw the picture, he thought it so beautiful that he greatly desired to marry the woman whose portrait it was. He commanded his retainers, saying, "Since this picture has been painted, this beautiful woman must surely exist somewhere. You must go and find her for me."

The retainers took the picture and went about from village to village, asking everyone they met if they knew where the woman whose portrait it was might be found. Finally they came to the village where Gombei lived. There they asked, "Do you know the woman who is painted here?" The villagers replied, "Yes, that woman is the wife of Gombei." The retainers went to the hut where Gombei lived, and there they found that the woman was exactly like the picture.

"The lord of the province has commanded us to take this woman with us," said the retainers, forcing her to go with them.

"Have mercy on me, please. Please have mercy on me," Gombei pleaded, but to no avail, and his wife was taken away. Gombei, stricken with grief, cried endlessly. His nose began to run. The mucous mixed with his tears and made a stream reaching clear to the ground. His wife too cried and cried. "Gombei," she sobbed, "there is no way out; I must go. But when the end of the year comes, you must come to the lord's castle and sell pine trees for the new year's gate decorations. If you do that, we can surely meet again." Saying this, she was taken away.

Soon the end of the year drew near. Gombei took a large bundle of young pine trees on his back and merrily set off for the lord's castle. When he came to the front gate of the castle, he called out in a loud voice, "Gate pines for sale! Gate pines for sale!"

As soon as she heard Gombei's voice outside, his wife, who until then had never even smiled, broke into merry laughter. The lord was so happy to see her laugh that he ordered his retainers to bring in the man selling pine trees. When Gombei was brought in, the woman again laughed happily.

The lord was overjoyed and said, "If you enjoy the pine tree peddler so much, I shall become one, and you shall be happier than ever." Saying this, he put his own robes on Gombei and took

Gombei's dirty rags and put them on. He loaded the pine trees on his back and danced about calling, "Gate pines for sale! Gate pines for sale!"

When she saw this, the woman looked happier than ever before and again burst out in laughter. The lord was so pleased that he went through the gates and outside the castle, walking along calling, "Gate pines for sale! Gate pines for sale!"

As soon as he was gone, the woman ordered the retainers to close the iron gates securely and lock them. After a short while the lord returned. When he found that the gates were shut, he was very surprised. Pounding on the doors of the gate, he called, "The lord is outside, the lord is outside," but no one would open the gates.

Inside the castle, Gombei and his wife, surrounded by many servants, spent the rest of their lives in peace and luxury.

Ichigo buranto kudatta. "The market was good; everything sold out."

·49· *The Golden Eggplant*

This tale shows much similarity to the plot of Type 707, The Three Golden Sons, although many of the incidents appearing in European versions are not found here. Motif S411.2, "Wife banished for some small fault," and S431, "Castoff wife exposed in boat," are the principal motifs. Kata No. 328, "The Gold-Bearing Tree." Collected on Sado Island, Niigata-ken, from Kin Nakagawa.

This tale of a calumniated wife is even more popular in Europe than is the tale of "The Girl without Arms," No. 30 in this collection. Thompson, p. 121, reports that a cursory examination of easily available reference works reveals 414 versions. He does not mention it being found in Japan but does state that it is known in India and Siberia.

The Japanese variants have the motif of banishment and restoration, but the motivation of the plot lacks the complication of European versions, and the tale as found in Japan may not ac-

tually be very closely related to European tradition. It is chiefly in the southern part of Japan that the eight versions available have been recorded. Ikeda, p. 198, states that it is told in Okinawa as a legend about a fifteenth-century ruler.

• LONG AGO in a certain place there lived an old man and his wife. One day when the old man went to the beach to gather seaweed, he saw a boat made from a hollowed out log come floating by. He looked into the boat, and there he saw a young lady. She was so weak that she was hardly breathing because she had spent many days floating on the sea.

The old man took the young woman and returned home with her. He and his wife nursed her very carefully. She was soon completely well again and was very grateful for their kindness. Since they had no children of their own, they decided to keep her as their own daughter and heir.

The young woman had been expecting a baby when she was put into the boat to float on the sea. It was not long before she gave birth to a baby boy as beautiful as a jewel. The old man and his wife were filled with joy.

When the boy grew to be a young lad of seven or eight years old, he would sometimes say to his mother, "All my playmates have both a father and a mother; I have only a grandfather, a grandmother, and a mother; why is it that I have no father?" But his mother would not tell him the reason.

One day she finally told him her story. "Your mother was formerly the wife of the lord of a certain country. I was young then and talented, and my husband loved me very much. However, some of my friends were jealous of me. One day they took some dry husks of thatching grass and put them under the lord's bed. The lord, not knowing they were there, got into the bed, and the hulls broke with a sound, *pichi,* as though someone were breaking wind. When the other women heard the sound, they said that I had broken wind in the presence of the lord. The lord became so angry that he put me in a boat and set me adrift in the sea. And so, my son, that lord was your father."

After this, the young man begged his mother every day to allow him to go to the country where the lord ruled. He begged so hard that finally she could do nothing but let him go. He was given two gold coins each worth one *isshu* for his traveling expenses, and so he set off.

First he went down to the beach and, taking a rock, broke one of the coins into little pieces. He wrapped the grains of gold in a piece of paper and put them into the fold of his kimono. He then set off for the country where the lord ruled.

When he arrived at the lord's castle, he began marching around and around the castle calling out,

Seeds from the golden tree for sale!
Seeds from the golden tree for sale!

Every day he marched around and around the castle crying his wares as loud as he could. At first no one paid any attention to him, but finally the lord heard him. He commanded his retainers: "That sounds like an unusual peddler. Bring him in and let us try what he is selling." The young man was brought in, and the lord asked him, "What are those seeds from a golden tree?"

From the fold of his kimono, the young man took the paper in which he had carefully wrapped the grains of gold from the *isshu* coin. Opening the paper, he showed the gold to the lord, saying, "These seeds are from a golden tree. If one plants them in the ashes of a charcoal brazier and fertilizes them every day with tea, a sprout will come up and grow into a great golden tree with as much silver and golden fruit as anyone could desire. However, unless they are planted by someone who has never once in his life broken wind, they will not sprout at all."

"Why you must be crazy," the lord replied mockingly; "there is no one in the whole world who has not broken wind at least once."

"Well then," said the boy, "why did you punish my mother so severely, setting her adrift on the sea, just because you thought she once broke wind?"

And so the lord realized for the first time that the young man was his own son. He had no other children and was overjoyed at finding his son, declaring that the young man should become his heir.

• 50 • The Bundles of Straw and the King's Son

Motifs N421.1, "Progressive lucky bargains," and S411.2, "Wife banished for some small fault," belong here. Kata No. 201, "The Straw Rich Man." Collected on Okierabu Island, Oshima-gun, Kagoshima-ken, from Kubomori Sashi.

Ikeda, p. 204, assigns this tale to Type 736, Luck and Wealth, although the plot is considerably different from that given in the type-index. Thompson, p. 142, states that European versions of Type 736 are primarily literary, being based on the Arabian Nights and medieval European tradition. A closely related tale is old in Japanese tradition, appearing in the Konjaku Monogatori, an eleventh-century collection of Indian, Chinese, and native Japanese tales. It is also included in the Uji Shui, a thirteenth-century collection. The tale is represented in Japanese oral tradition by some twenty-four versions.

The request that the boy observe the first seven days after his mother's death is a manifestation of the Buddhist belief that the soul does not begin its journey to the other world until the seventh day following death. Cf. No. 29, "The White Bird Sister."

• LONG AGO in the city of Naha on the island of Okinawa, there lived a woman and her young son. When the child was only seven years old, the mother became very sick. As she lay dying, she called her boy to her and said, "I am going to die, my child, and I have no property to leave to you except three bundles of *mochi* rice straw [glutinous rice straw], which are up in the attic of the storeroom. That is your legacy. On the seventh day after I die, you must take the rice straw to the *miso* [salty malted bean paste] shop and exchange it for some *miso*. Now I shall tell you about the straw.

"When I was the king's wife, there were a great number of

people working for the king. I was once looking out toward the sea when I saw a great ship sailing in the distance. I cried out, 'Oh, what a magnificent ship!' All the people stopped working to look at the ship. The king became very angry and said that any woman who caused so many people to waste so much time should be expelled from the palace, and so I was sent out of the palace. When I left, I was given these three bundles of *mochi* rice straw by the king's father." Saying this, the boy's mother died.

On the seventh day after his mother's death, the boy took the three bundles of *mochi* rice straw and went to the *miso* shop as his mother had told him. However, no one came to exchange anything with him. He sat there for two days, then three days; finally the master of the shop gave in and asked him if he would sell the straw. He gave him three *sho* [about one and one-half gallons] of *miso* for it.

Taking the *miso*, the boy next went to a tinker's shop. He sat by the door of the shop for a whole day, and finally the owner of the shop said, "Won't you give me that *miso*?"

"This *miso* is the only property that I have," replied the boy; "I couldn't give it to you unless you gave me something."

"Well then," said the tinker, "please sell it to me."

"No, I don't want to sell it either. But if you will give me one of those kettles, I will trade the *miso* for it."

"Well, if it's a kettle you want, you may take any one you like."

"Then give me that old cracked one with the broken edge, and I shall give you the *miso*," said the boy, and so he received the broken kettle.

Next he went to a blacksmith shop where he sat by the door for two whole days. The blacksmith finally came and said to him, "Will you sell me that kettle you have?"

"I cannot sell the kettle," replied the boy, "but I will exchange it for a sword if you wish."

"What sort of sword would you like?" asked the blacksmith.

"If you will give me an old dull sword, I shall trade you the kettle," said the boy, and so he received an old dull sword that had no handle.

Next he went to the beach where a Chinese ship was anchored. Being quite tired, he lay down on the beach to take a nap, and a thief came along. Seeing the sword by the boy's pillow, he thought he would steal it, but when he put out his hand to take the sword, it became a snake. Every time he tried to take the sword, it would turn into a snake, and so he was unable to steal it.

The captain of the ship saw from a distance what was happening and called out to the boy, "Hallo! Boy, bring your sword and come on board my ship."

When the boy came on board the ship, the captain said, "Won't you please sell me your sword."

"I would sell the sword," said the boy, "but I wonder if you have as much money as I want for it."

"Why, in a Chinese ship such as this, there is any amount of money. I can give you as much as you wish."

"Well, I really do not want to sell it for money anyway," said the boy, "but I will exchange it for one of your folding screens."

"Well, if it is a folding screen that you would like, there are any number of them. Just choose any one you like."

"Then I should like to have that ragged, torn one," said the boy, and so it was given to him.

He took the broken screen and set off for the palace of a king named Kanashi. He went into the palace garden and set up the screen on a little hill in the garden; then he lay down in its shade to take a nap. When he did this, the nightingales which were painted on the screen began to sing. Soon a great number of birds gathered about the screen chirping and singing.

When the king saw this, he called the boy and said, "Boy, won't you sell me that screen?"

"I am sorry, but I cannot sell this screen," said the boy, "but I will exchange it for two things."

"What are those two things?" asked the king.

"All the waves of the sea and all the water in your kingdom," replied the boy.

When the king heard this he thought that the boy must surely be crazy, but he immediately had a certificate made out authorizing the boy to control all the water in the sea and on the land.

And so it came about that when anyone wanted to draw fresh

water, they had to pay the boy ten *sen,* and if they wanted to use water from the sea, they had to pay five *sen.* The people of the kingdom soon became very tired of having to pay every time they wanted to use some water and sent a petition to the king asking that the water be made free again. The king realized that he had been wrong to let the boy control the people's water supply. He called the lad to him and said, "I will give you any amount of money if you will let the people use the water freely again."

The boy, however, refused to listen to the king's pleading, and so the king said, "Very well, then, let us have a battle, and the winner shall control the water."

"I am not afraid to fight," said the boy, "but first I should like to ask the king one question. When my mother was the king's wife and she was forced to leave the palace because she was said to have distracted the workmen, who was it that drove her out of the palace?"

When the boy said this the king realized for the first time who the boy was and said, "I shall let you be king if you allow the people to use their water freely again."

And so the king went into retirement and relinquished his kingdom to the boy.

• 51 • *The Boy Who Told Tall Tales*

Motif J31, "Encounter with clever children (woman) dissuades man from visit," is the central theme. Kata No. 316, "The Child Who Told Tall Tales." Collected in Satsuma-gun, Kagoshima-ken.

Sixteen versions of this tale have been collected in Japan. It is often told in connection with Sogi, a well-known fifteenth-century poet and priest.

Shumi Mountain is a high mountain which, according to Buddhist legend, is located in the center of the earth.

The strainer used in making miso [*malted soybean paste*] *is*

*generally woven of bamboo and is usually about one foot in
diameter.*

• THERE WAS A man who was very skillful at telling tall tales. In
the neighboring village there was a man who was also very good
at telling such stories. One evening the neighboring man came
over to exchange tales, but the man was gone, and there was just
one child at home.

"Is anyone at home?" called the neighbor.

"Yes."

"Where is your father?"

"He's gone to climb Shumi Mountain. He took some incense
and left a good while ago."

Knowing that the boy was telling a story, the man asked,
"Where is your mother?"

"They say that a whale has come to the beach out behind the
village, and she has gone to scoop it up with a *miso* strainer."
The neighboring man did not wish to be outdone and said, "I
threw a big stone mortar from Oose; it didn't land around here,
did it?"

"Yes, it did. Just a short while ago, it hit here and got caught
in a spider's web."

So finally the man from the neighboring village had to leave
in defeat.

Soon the boy's father returned home. "Did anyone come today?" he asked. "Yes, the storyteller from the neighboring village came, but I told him some stories and he ran back home,"
replied the boy.

The father became very angry and cried, "What a wicked
thing to have done!" He put the boy in a straw bag and took
him off to drown him in the sea.

On the way he had to pass by a friend's house, so he stopped
in to smoke a pipe of tobacco with him. He put the straw bag
down on the ground. While he was gone, someone came by and
stepped on the bag. "Who is that stepping on me?" called the
boy.

"What are you doing there in that bag?"

"I am in this bag to heal my eyes."

"Does it cure one's eyes to get in a straw bag like that?"

"Oh, yes!"

"Then let me do it."

The man was a mackerel peddler, and his eyes were quite bad. The boy put the mackerel peddler in the bag and in exchange for that took the mackerel. "While you are in the bag, you must not say anything," he said and ran off.

When evening came he dipped himself in some water and then went home. "Father, father, you would have been more clever to have thrown me farther out in the ocean; then I could have caught more mackerel," and he showed his father the fish he had brought.

"Then next time you can throw me in," said his father.

·52· *A Tall Tale Contest*

Motifs X905, "Lying contests," and X1423.1, "Lie: the great cabbage," are the principal motifs here. Kata No. 315, "The Boasting Match." Collected in Amakusa-gun, Kumamoto-ken, from Isamu Yamashita.

Tall tales whose point consists in one lie being topped by another are world-wide. Thompson, p. 216, cites the tall tale, involving X1423.1, in which the description of a huge cabbage is countered by the detailing of a huge kettle in which to cook it. This tale is told throughout Europe and in India and Indochina. The Japanese text given here as a local legend is known throughout Japan, being told about a variety of different places. Eight versions of the tale have been recorded. Dorson, in Folk Legends of Japan, *p. 207, has a variant.*

The three men in this tale were lords of their respective provinces. Their names are actually the names of feudal provinces in southern Japan.

The standard unit of floor measurement is a tatami *mat, which is about three by six feet. An ordinary-sized room usually contains from four and one-half to eight mats.*

Lake Biwa is the largest lake in Japan. It is located several hundred miles north of the old province of Mino.

• Higo-*sama*, Satsuma-*sama*, and Mino-*sama* made a pilgrimage to Ise. At Ise they stopped at an inn, but they could not decide who should sit in the place of honor.

"Since we can't decide who sits there, let's have a contest to see who can tell the biggest story. Whoever tells the tallest tale shall sit in the place of honor," said one of them. "That's a good idea; I agree," said another, and so they decided to tell stories.

"Please, you begin," said one. "No, you begin," said another, and so no one would volunteer to start first. "This will never do," they said, and so they called one of the inn maids. When she came they said, "We've decided to have a tall tale contest, but no one will start first; please go and make some lots. Number them one, two, and three."

The maid went and, taking some paper, twisted it into a string and made three lots, then brought them to the three men. "Here, I have finished them. Please, someone draw one," she said.

"You go first." "No, you go first," and no one would draw first. "Well, then I shall draw one first," said Higo-*sama,* and he drew one. "Which one was it," they asked, and when he looked at it, it was number three. Next Satsuma-*sama* drew. His lot turned out to be number one. "Then Mino-*sama* doesn't need to draw; he'll be number two anyway," they said.

"Well, Satsuma-*sama,* you are first, so please start," said Higo-*sama.*

"There is nothing unusually big in Satsuma, except that there is a big camphor tree. The inside of it is hollow, and there is a room the size of a hundred mats in it," said Satsuma-*sama*.

"That is a huge thing, all right," the others said in praise.

Next it was Mino-*sama's* turn to tell a story. "There is nothing particularly big in the country of Mino, except there is a rather big ox," said Mino-*sama*.

"How big is it?" the other two asked.

"Well, this ox is so big that it can stand in the country of Mino and drink Lake Biwa, which lies in the country of Oomi, dry in one gulp."

"That's quite a story all right," exclaimed the others in surprise.

"The others have told such good tales, I hardly know how to tell anything better than that," said Higo-*sama* to himself, cocking his head to one side to think.

The other two began to cough a bit impatiently. "We're waiting," they said.

"Well," said Higo-*sama*, "there is nothing especially big in the country of Higo, except that there are two cedar trees."

"How big are these cedar trees?" they asked.

"These two cedar trees grew so fast that in two or three years they had grown beyond the clouds."

"Oh, really? And why did they grow so tall?"

"Well, we intended to cut down the camphor tree which is growing in the country of Satsuma and make a drum body, then take the hide of the ox which is in the country of Mino and stretch it out for a drum head, and then use these two cedar trees as drum sticks."

With that, Higo-*sama* was given the place of honor to sit in. It is still said that he is more worthy of honor than the lords of Satsuma and Mino.

•53• *The Mountain Where Old People Were Abandoned*

Type 981, Wisdom of Hidden Old Man Saves Kingdom. Kata No. 329, "The Mountain Where Old People Were Abandoned." Collected in Iida-mura, Shimoina-gun, Nagano-ken, from the mother of collector Kiyomi Suzuki.

The motif of abandonment of the aged appears in the eleventh-century Konjaku Monogatori *in a tale derived from India. More than forty variants of this motif have been found in Japan; not all have the sequel of the tests solved by the rescued elder. Dorson has a text of this legend in his* Folk Tales of Japan, *pp. 223–25, with references on pp. 222–23 to the powerful short novel by Shichiro Fukasawa based on this theme, first translated into English by John Bester in* Japan Quarterly, *IV (1957), 200–232, and later adapted into a Kabuki play and a motion picture. Donald Keene has included his translation of Fukasawa's novel in his recent collection of three modern Japanese short novels,* The Old Woman, the Wife, and the Archer. *Keene's introduction, pp. xi–xiii, contains an excellent discussion of the central motif of the tale and its relationship to past and present Japanese life. He notes that the Japanese have undoubtedly found this story a painful one but that they have never forgotten or suppressed it. He supposes that despite the respect paid to the aged in modern Japan, memories of an ancient past still lurk in people's minds.*

The tale is scattered throughout Europe. Thompson, pp. 266–67, remarks that it is often ascribed to King Solomon. Eberhard, pp. 115–17, lists six variants from China, and Thompson and Roberts, p. 123, give five from India.

• LONG AGO when people had reached the age of sixty and were unable to do anything, they were thrown into a mountain canyon. This was known as "sixty canyon abandonment."

In a certain village there was a farmer who became sixty years old. Since the lord of the country had commanded it, the time had arrived for him to be thrown into the mountain canyon. The man's son took him on his back and set off for the mountains. They continued farther and farther into the mountains. As they went along, the old man, riding on his son's back, broke off the tips of tree branches in order to mark the trail. "Father, father, what are you doing that for? Is it so you can find your way back home?" asked the son.

"No, it would be too bad if you were unable to find your way home," replied the father, "so I am marking the trail for you."

When he heard this the son realized how kindhearted his father was, and so he returned home with him. They hid the old man under the porch so that the lord would know nothing about it.

Now the lord of the country sometimes commanded his subjects to do very difficult things. One day he gathered all the farmers of the village together and said, "You must each bring me a rope woven from ashes."

All the farmers were very troubled, knowing that they could not possibly weave a rope from ashes. The young farmer whom we just mentioned went back home, called to his father under the porch, and said, "Today the lord commanded that everyone bring a rope woven from ashes. How can we do this?"

"You must weave a rope very tightly, then carefully burn it until it turns to ashes; then you can take it to the lord," said the old man.

The young farmer, happy to get this advice, did just as he was told. He made a rope of ashes and took it to the lord. None of the other farmers were able to do it, and so this farmer alone had carried out the lord's instructions. For this the lord praised him highly.

Next the lord commanded, "Everyone must bring a conch shell with a thread passed through it."

The young farmer went to his father again and asked him what he should do. "Take a conch shell and point the tip toward the light; then take a thread and stick a piece of rice on it. Give the rice to an ant and make it crawl into the mouth of the shell; in this way you can get the thread through."

The young farmer did as he was told, and so got the thread through the conch shell. He took the shell to the lord, who was much impressed. "How were you able to do such a difficult thing?" he asked.

The young farmer replied: "Actually I was supposed to throw my old father down into the mountain canyon, but I felt so sorry for him that I brought him back home and hid him under the porch. The things that you asked us to do were so difficult that I had to ask my father how to do them. I have done them as he told me, and brought them to you," and he honestly told what had happened.

When the lord heard this he was very much impressed and realized that old people are very wise and that they should be well taken care of. After that he commanded that the "sixty canyon abandonment" be stopped.

·54· *The Three-Year Sleeping Boy*

Type 1462, The Unwilling Suitor Advised from Tree. Kata No. 195, "The Gambler Son-in-law." Collected in Kami Kuishiki-mura, Nishi Yatsushiro-gun, Yamanashi-ken, from Kesa Kono. The title is derived from a proverbial expression used to describe an extremely lazy child.

Twenty-one versions of this tale are recorded in Japan. It is found in the thirteenth-century collection, Uji Shui, and is the subject of a celebrated dramatization by Junji Kinoshita, pp. 5–42.

The tale is not well known outside Japan. Four variants have been reported from Norway and one from India.

• ONCE LONG ago in a certain place there were two houses side by side. In the house to the east lived a very wealthy man while the people who lived in the house to the west were very, very poor. In the west house, the father had died some time before; only the mother and her one son lived there. The son was very lazy; he did nothing every day but eat and sleep, eat and sleep, and so everyone in the neighborhood called him Eat-Sleep.

His mother could not bear to see him doing nothing at all, so she would sometimes try to find work for him, saying, "If it weren't for my making some money, we would be in trouble." But he would only say, "Now, mother, I have a plan," and would just go on eating and sleeping.

After a while the young man became twenty-one years old. One day when his mother was going to town to sell some charcoal, he said to her, "Mother, if you're going to town, please buy me a priest's hat and kimono."

"What are you going to do with them?" she asked, and he said, "Oh, I have a plan," and he would not tell her why he wanted them. His mother had no idea why he wanted them, but she thought that if she got them for him, he might possibly start working; so when she went to town, she got him the priest's hat and kimono.

The young man put on the priest's hat and kimono, disguised his face, and sneaked into the neighboring rich man's house. He climbed up and hid behind the shrine on the *kamidana* [household Shinto shrine]. When evening came and the rich man's family were all eating dinner, he suddenly jumped down from the *kamidana*. Everyone was very surprised and asked, "Who are you?"

Disguising his voice, the young man said, "I am this village's *ujigami* [tutelary deity]. I have ordained that your daughter and the son of the house to the west must be married. You must see that this is done as soon as possible. If they do not get married, I will turn them both into clay." While everyone was still speechless with surprise, he ran from the room and disappeared.

The rich man's family thought that if this were really the *ujigami,* he would be returning to the village shrine, so they hurriedly sent some servants after him to bid him farewell, but the young man had already run home, so the servants were unable to find him anywhere.

The rich man waited until morning; then he immediately sent messengers to the house to the west. They asked that the rich man's daughter be taken in marriage since it was the *ujigami's* command. The mother of the house to the west was greatly surprised and refused, saying, "We can't do that; it would not be right for us, as poor as we are, to take the daughter of the rich man."

The rich man, however, insisted, saying, "We urge you to take her; you must take her. No matter how poor you are, we will rebuild your house and make it as good as ours. Please do not worry about that."

"Well then, all right," said the mother, finally agreeing.

Soon woodcutters, carpenters, and plasterers were sent to the house to the west, and it was completely rebuilt; then a splendid wedding was held. Some time afterward the Eat-Sleep young man said to his mother, "See, I had a good plan, didn't I?"

·55· *The Nun as Judge*

Motif J1795, "Image in mirror mistaken for picture," is applicable here. Kata No. 416, "The Nun's Arbitration." Collected in Kuzumaki-mura, Minami Kanbara-gun, Niigata-ken, from Etsu Makino.

Fifteen versions of this tale have been collected in Japan. Texts without the arbitration of the nun have been recorded in England and the United States.

· IN A CERTAIN place there was a young man who loved his parents very much. He married and shortly afterwards his father died, so that he was very sad.

One time he had to go up to Edo on business, and there he saw a mirror shop. Wondering what sort of unusual things were sold there, he looked into one of the mirrors. He saw his own reflection, which looked exactly like his own father. He was very surprised and said, "I didn't know that my father would be here!" He bought one of the mirrors and took it home. After he got home, he put it up in the *butsudan* [household Buddhist shrine] and prayed before it every day.

One day his wife said to herself, "What is my husband doing, looking into the *butsudan* all day?" She went to look for herself. She found that there was a woman's face in the mirror. She became very angry and said to her husband, "Old man, nobody but you would do a thing like this. You bring a concubine home and put her inside this gold frame!"

"What are you saying! That is my dead father," and the two of them began quarreling back and forth.

Just then a nun came by. After she had found out what they were arguing about, she said, "Please let me take a look." And when she looked in the mirror, she saw a nun there. "Oh, the woman has repented and become a nun, so you can pardon her," she said.

And so that was the end of the argument.

· 56 · *The Clever Lord*

Type 1537, The Corpse Killed Five Times. Kata No. 259, "Clever Yasohachi." Collected in Kuzumaki-mura, Minami Kanbara-gun, Niigata-ken, from Etsu Makino.

Thompson, p. 208, reports that "This well-known fabliau and medieval jest is told all over Europe and a good part of Asia, and is known in Africa and in America, both in European and American Indian tradition." The tale is represented in Japanese oral tradition by at least eight versions. Zong In-sob, pp. 197 ff., has a good version in his collection of Korean tales.

· A CERTAIN man came home late one night and found his wife talking with a man. "What a brazen fellow that is," he thought to himself and entered the house. He struck the man on the back such a blow that, without meaning to, he killed him. When he looked and saw who it was, he found that it was the master from the village.

The man and his wife wondered what they should do. Finally they decided that it would be best to ask the clever lord for advice, and so they went to ask him.

"All right, all right," said the clever lord; "I will take care of it," and he took the dead master on his back and went to the place where some of the young men of the village were gambling. He stood the dead master up in front of the storm shutters, made a rattling sound, *koto koto,* on the doors, and then fled.

The young men inside said, "Someone is peeking at us," and one of them took a stick and crept outside; then he went up behind the man standing at the window and struck him a good blow. When he did this the body fell with a thud, and all the others came out to see what had happened. When they found that it was the master from the village, they cried, "We have done a terrible thing; we have killed the master!"

They were all very worried. They decided to go and ask the clever lord what they should do.

The clever lord said, "All right, all right, I will take care of it." This time he carried the dead body to the master's house. He went to the front door and called, "Wife, I've returned now; please open the door."

"You do nothing but play around all night like this; you don't need to come home at all," cried his wife.

"Then I will jump in the well and kill myself," said the clever lord, and taking the body, he threw it down the well, then fled.

The wife thought that her husband had thrown himself down the well for sure and cried, "If I had opened the door for you, such a thing as this would not have happened." Finally she decided to go ask the clever lord what to do.

The clever lord said, "I will take care of it for you; don't worry about it at all." He heated up a kettle of water and put the master in a rice steamer; then he steamed him for a while. Next he called a doctor saying, "The master has a very, very bad fever." The doctor came as fast as he could. He felt of the master's pulse and said, "It is a pity, but he has died." So, finally, they could have a funeral for him.

The clever lord received all sorts of gifts as payment from everyone he had helped, and so he made great profit from it all.

·57· *The Hawk Fledgling*

The general motif J1675, "Clever dealing with a king," is present here. Collected in Yusuhara-mura, Takaoka-gun, Kochi-ken.

This is one of a group of anecdotes about a clever man which are widespread throughout southern Japan. The man goes by various names in different districts but his exploits are of such a nature that they are generally grouped together as Hikoichi or Kichiyomu stories. Junji Kinoshita has written a drama based on the adventures of Hikoichi, pp. 56–88.

Because of the inordinate amount of protocol involved in relations with officialdom in feudal Japan, the visit of a high government official to a rural village entailed extensive preparation and expense on the part of the villagers. The inhabitants of Koreichi's village were understandably distressed at the thought of such a visit.

• ONE TIME Koreichi went to take the yearly rice tax to the lord of the province. The lord wanted to have a hawk fledgling and asked him if he could get one for him in his village. Koreichi soon agreed to do so. "That will be easy to do; there is a nest of young hawks in the mountain just behind my house. Please come to the village sometime and get one." The lord was glad to hear that his long-standing wish would be fulfilled and promised that he would soon come there for an inspection tour and would get the fledgling then.

Koreichi returned to his village and told the leaders of the village what had happened. They were all filled with consternation. "How will we entertain the lord when he comes? Where will we get the money?" they asked among themselves, and the problem became the cause of a daily headache to the whole village.

Koreichi was sorry that he had started the whole affair and said that if the lord's coming would be so much trouble he would go immediately and withdraw the invitation to come. The villagers told him that he couldn't just go and tell the lord not to come, but he said that he would think of something. He set off for the castle town as if he hadn't a care in the world.

Finally, after two days, he got to the castle town and immediately went to the lord's castle. The lord was very happy to see him and said, "Is the hawk fledgling growing up well?"

"Yes, it is getting bigger and bigger. Recently it has begun to call, *pinyo pinyo,* all the time."

The lord began to laugh loudly. "Well, you must have been mistaken; that is a kite, not a hawk. There's no use going to get it," and he decided not to go there for an inspection tour.

Soon after that Koreichi went back to his village and told what had happened. Everyone was very much relieved.

·58· *Stinginess*

The general motif W152, "Stinginess," is applicable. Kata No. 380, "Stinginess." Collected in Oita-ken.

This anecdote is one of the Hikoichi-Kichiyomu cycle; see the note on "The Hawk Fledgling," No. 57 above.

• KICHIYOMU SAID to his wife, "Wife, go over to the neighbors and borrow a hammer. There is a nail in the veranda which is sticking out, and it is dangerous."

The wife went over to the neighbors and soon came back empty-handed. "When I went to the neighbors, they asked me whether the nail we wanted to pound was bamboo, or wood, or iron. When I said that it was an iron nail, they said that in that case it would be apt to ruin their hammer, and they wouldn't loan it to me."

Kichiyomu scowled. "There are really some stingy people in this world. Well, there is nothing else to do; get out our hammer; we'll have to use our own."

·59· *It's Been Well Used*

The general motif J1805, "Other misunderstandings of words," applies here. Kata No. 392, "Mis-hearing." Collected in Toka-machi-mura, Minami Uonuma-gun, Niigata-ken, from Matsu Narito.

Anecdotes of this nature are widespread in Japan and are told in mixed audiences or in the presence of children without embarrassment.

The widely used euphemism daiji na tokoro, "important place," is employed here as in "The Oni's Laughter," No. 16 above.

Japanese country women sometimes wear no closely fitting undergarments such as are used in Western countries. The square

*of cloth wrapped about the hips under the kimono offers little
protection when squatting.*

• LONG AGO in a certain place there was an old woman. One day
when the weather was fine, she took a large stoneware jar to the
river to wash it. She squatted down to wash the jar, and her important place was showing.

Just then one of the young men of the village came by. The
old woman didn't know that her important place was showing,
and the young man thought he ought to warn her so that everyone wouldn't be seeing it. He knew he shouldn't tell her directly,
and so he said, "Grandmother, you have it out today."

"Yes, the weather is so nice, you know," said the old lady.

Since the old woman apparently didn't understand what he
meant, he tried again, "It certainly is big."

"It's the biggest there is," said the old woman.

"It's very black," said the young man.

"Yes, it's been well used," she said.

The young man gave up and left.

•60• *The Pillow*

*Motif J1805.2, "Unusual word misunderstood," is central. Col-
lected in Kamihei-gun, Iwate-ken.*

*There are a large number of jokes about stupid or rustic bride-
grooms. These anecdotes are often salacious.*

*Pronouns are rarely used in Japanese. When the son-in-law
related his experience with* okoma, *the family would have understood it to mean no one but the girl. For this reason the feminine
rather than the neuter pronoun has been supplied in the translation. The Japanese word for pillow is* makura.

• A RATHER stupid son-in-law went to visit his wife's family.
There for the first time in his life he slept on a pillow. His head
felt so funny that he couldn't get to sleep. "What is this thing

anyway," he asked. His bride thought that he was asking what her name was, and she said, "It is Okoma."

The next morning when they got up, the whole family was eating breakfast together. The son-in-law said, "My, my, last night I just couldn't sleep a wink. I tried to get on *okoma,* but when I pushed her, she kept getting away and getting away until finally I got her up next to the wall and got on, then went to sleep."

It was a wooden block pillow that he was using.

•61• *There's No Deity There*

The general motif J1250, "Clever verbal retorts—general," is pertinent. Kata No. 340, "There's No Deity on the Priest's Head." Collected in Ozuya-mura, Ninohe-gun, Iwate-ken, from Genji Sato.

There are a large number of anecdotes about priests and acolytes in which the acolyte generally manages to get the better of the priest. These anecdotes, usually a play on words, are often told on an acolyte named Ikkyu-san and are favorite material for children's books. An American variant to the present tale is given in the Introduction, p. xii.

Buddhist priests' heads are shaven, and so the acolyte was correct in asserting that there was no kami, "hair," on the priest's head.

• LONG AGO the priest and an acolyte of a certain temple were going on some religious business. The acolyte had to urinate. He stood by the edge of the road and started to open up the front of his kimono, but the priest said, "Stop, stop! The deity of the road is there; don't do it there."

They went a little farther, and when the acolyte started to urinate in a field by the edge of the road, the priest cried, "Stop! Stop! The deity of the harvest is there; don't do it there."

"I can't hold it any longer; I'll do it in the river," said the acolyte, but the priest said, "The water deity is in the river; don't do it there."

The acolyte wanted to urinate so badly that he didn't care any more where he did it and went over to a roadside image of Jizo-sama [Buddhist guardian deity of children], but the priest cried, "Nobody would ever do it there!" and he scolded him soundly.

Finally the acolyte could hold it no longer, and he began to urinate, *zaa zaa,* on the priest's head. "What are you doing?" cried the priest.

"There is no *kami* [homophone; deity or hair] on your head so it's all right," said the acolyte, and he kept right on urinating.

Dondo harai. "With this, it's sold out."

.62. *The Sweet* Mochi's *Parents*

The general motif J1500 "Clever practical retort" applies to this story. Kata Nos. 332, 333, and 341, "A Razor Swims," "The White Eggplant's Father," and "Horse Dung." Collected in Nibukawa-mura, Ono-gun, Gifu-ken, from Shizu Hirata.

This tale is another in the priest-acolyte cycle described above. Priests in Japan are subject to the same sort of risqué jokes as are parsons in European folk tradition.

• LONG AGO there was a priest who lived in a certain mountain temple. His lover lived a short distance away. One day the priest put some eggs in a tiered box and handed them to his acolyte. "There is some sweet *mochi* in this box; please take it to the woman's house," said the priest.

On the way, the acolyte opened the box and saw that there were eggs in it. Seeing that the priest had told him a lie, he took it on to the woman's house, laughing to himself.

Two or three days after this the priest wrapped up about ten sweetfish and gave them to the acolyte to take to the woman. He told him that the package contained a razor. On the way, the acolyte opened the package to see what it was and found that it was sweetfish. Laughing to himself, he gave it to the woman.

Five or six days after this the priest had some religious business
to attend to in his parish. He took the acolyte, and as they were
going along the road, they passed a farmer's house where there
were a lot of chickens. When the acolyte saw the chickens, he
said, "Oh, priest-*sama*, look, there are a lot of the parents of
sweet *mochi* like the ones I took to the woman's house for you
the other day."

The priest was embarrassed and said nothing but continued
on his way. After their business was over, they were on the way
home, and as they crossed the bridge over a river, there were
many sweetfish swimming in the water below. When the acolyte saw this, he cried with a loud voice, "Priest-*sama*, look down
at the river. There are a lot of razors swimming around down
there like the one I took to the woman's house the other day."

The priest realized that the acolyte had opened up the package of fish too, and he said, "You should see things and say nothing and hear things and say nothing. Now be quiet and follow
along behind me."

Soon they began to climb up the mountain pass. The wind
started to blow, and the priest's hat blew off. The acolyte had
been told, "See things and say nothing," so he purposely did not
pick up the hat and said nothing about it all the way back to
the temple. When they got there, the priest realized that his hat
was gone and thought that he had left it somewhere in the parish.

"Priest-*sama*, as we were coming home you told me to see
things and say nothing, just to keep quiet; so when the wind
blew your hat off, I didn't pick it up and didn't say anything,"
said the acolyte.

"I don't care what; go back and get the hat and bring it to
me," said the priest.

The acolyte went back along the road they had come. He
picked up the hat, put leaves and horse dung in it, and took it
home. When the priest saw it, he cried angrily, "What did you
put those dirty things in it for?"

"You told me, "I don't care what; go pick it up and bring it
here,' so I picked up anything I saw in the road and brought it
here," said the boy.

The priest became angrier still. "Horse dung and stuff like that is dirty. Take the hat and wash it away."

The acolyte took the hat to the river and let it float away. After two or three days the priest again had some business, and he hunted for his hat but couldn't find it. "Acolyte, do you know where my hat is?"

"Priest-*sama*, you told me to take the hat and wash it away, so I washed it away along with the horse dung. The hat is gone now."

•63• Bedding in One's Ear

Kata No. 343, "Bedding in One's Ear." Collected in Ushirogawa-mura, Hata-gun, Kochi-ken.

This is another priest-acolyte anecdote as described above.

To be so poor as to lack futon to sleep on is, in Japanese tales, a favorite way of describing abject poverty.

• LONG AGO in a certain place a priest and an acolyte lived alone in a temple. The temple was so poor that it is hardly worth telling about. They had no *futon* [padded bedding] at all to sleep on, and so every night they would crawl into a pile of straw and sleep that way. The priest warned the acolyte, "When a guest comes, you must never mention about our sleeping in straw."

One morning very early one of the parishioners came. Hurriedly the priest jumped out of the straw and quickly changed his clothes, then invited the guest in. He called to the boy in the kitchen, "Bring some tea." When the acolyte brought the tea, he happened to see that there was a straw stuck to the priest's ear. It looked so funny that he could hardly stand it, and he said, "Priest-*sama*, there is a piece of *futon* stuck to your ear."

Glossary

bakemono A bogey, a demon. A malevolent spirit often assuming animal form. The word is often used as a generic term for any malevolent ogre.

butsudan The household Buddhist shrine, usually a cabinet or an alcove in which ancestor name tablets and various religious relics are kept.

choja A wealthy landowner. The two chief protagonists of a tale are often *choja*. One is generally named Agari, 'Sunrise,' and is usually very wealthy and evil. The other is called Iri, 'Sunset,' and is a poor but honest man. In tales it is possible for a *choja* to have lost his wealth and still be known as *choja*.

-danna Literally, "master." A suffix of respect now usually used toward the head of a household by the women and servants of the house. In feudal periods it was used by men to someone of higher rank.

-don; -dono A suffix of familiarity used by men among close acquaintances or to inferiors, never to superiors. The term was formerly one of respect; it degenerated to one of familiarity and is now seldom used.

dondo hare; dondo harai; dotto harai Dialect versions of a stylized story ending. Literally, "with this, it's sold out." The phrase seems to have originated with market stall holders, but is now used merely to signify the end of a story.

furoshiki A square of cloth used to wrap packages for carrying.

futon Heavy, padded comforters. Thicker ones are used as mattresses; somewhat thinner ones serve as bed covers. The

199

futon are spread out upon retiring and rolled up and stored during the day.

hakama Wide, loosely fitting trousers worn by men over the kimono.

hifukidake A mouth bellows. Literally, "fire-blowing bamboo." It is made from a section of bamboo; the mouth piece is open, and the other end has a pin hole to emit the stream of air. It is often endowed with magical properties.

ichibu A coin of the feudal period, equal in value to one-fourth of a *ryo*.

Jizo-sama The Buddhist guardian deity of children. Roadside statues of Jizo are very common throughout Japan.

kamidana The household Shinto shrine. Literally, "deity-shelf." It is often in the shape of a miniature temple and is attached to the wall near the ceiling. Periodic offerings of various types are placed before it. Not to be confused with the *butsudan*. Most older homes have both types of shrines.

Kannon The Buddhist goddess of mercy. One of the best known of the Buddhist deities; numerous temples are dedicated to her.

kibi dango A type of *mochi* which is made from a mixture of millet and rice rather than from rice alone.

koban A coin of the feudal period, also known as a *ryo*. It was of comparatively high value; exact value depended on the period. See also *oban*.

kobito Literally, "little people." Tiny, non-malevolent supernatural beings, smaller than dwarfs or brownies but of similar characteristics.

manju A steamed dumpling filled with meat or sweet bean paste, originally a Chinese dish.

miso A salty, malted soybean paste used chiefly as a soup stock.

mochi A heavy, semisolid dough made by pounding steamed glutinous rice. It is a delicacy considered indispensable to traditional celebrations but is also eaten at other times.

mon A coin of very·low value; in the feudal era, the smallest unit of money. It was equal to one-tenth of a *sen*.

-morai A suffix of familarity used among men, equivalent of *dono*.

nengumai A yearly tax of rice. A percentage of the rice harvest paid by the tenant farmer to the landowner, the amount varied from 10 to 50 per cent.

Neinya The paradise or dragon kingdom at the bottom of the sea; also known as *Neriya, Nira,* and *Ryugu. Ryugu* is a word of Chinese origin and is translated literally as "Dragon Palace." The other terms are native Japanese words; they are sometimes explained as referring to the dragon kingdom or to an undersea paradise. *Ryugu* is generally thought to be ruled by a king. A deity is sometimes the ruler of the undersea word when it is referred to as a paradise.

nibu A coin of the feudal era, valued at one-half of a *ryo.*

nushi The malevolent spirit of a swamp. Literally, "master." It is often represented by a snake which assumes the form of a woman.

oban The most valuable coin of the feudal period, ten times the value of a *koban* or *ryo.* Both the *oban* and *koban* were oblong in shape, the *oban* being approximately one inch wide and two inches long. Size and value varied with the historical period.

oni A malevolent, horned and tusked superhuman ogre of human form, but usually of some bright hue, generally red or blue. *Oni* are generally male and somewhat larger than humans. The word *oni* is sometimes applied to any ogre as a generic term.

Oni Island The island where *oni* are believed to live. They live in a paramilitary organization and are thought to make periodic raids on the land of human beings.

oni woman A malevolent female ogre. *Oni* are generally male ogres, but since the word *oni* can be a generic term, *oni* women may be the equivalent of *yamauba* [mountain ogress].

rokubu Literally, "six divisions." Itinerant religious ascetics, so named from their wandering throughout the sixty-six provinces of feudal Japan. A statue of the Buddha was carried on their backs and they stood in doorways and begged alms. The practice still exists.

ryo A coin of comparatively high value, the value depending on the period. A silver *ryo* contained about 15 to 20 grams of silver; gold *ryo* were also used. A *ryo* was also known as *koban*, and was equal to one-tenth of an *oban*.

Ryugu See *Neinya*.

sake An alcoholic beverage made from rice; rice wine. It is indispensable to any celebration and is used in many religious observances.

-sama A suffix of respect used toward deities or persons of high rank, also sometimes to one's parents and grandparents, and by a wife to her husband.

-san A suffix of courtesy. It is used to both men and women of rank equal with oneself, except that men generally do not use it to other men of close acquaintance. Children always use it to their elders; women generally use it to everyone except children or superiors, in which case *-chan* and *-sama*, respectively, are used.

samurai A warrior of the feudal period.

sen A coin of low value, one-hundredth of a *yen*.

suribachi A serrated grinding bowl, usually somewhat conical in shape.

tabi White canvaslike socks with a separated big toe for use with thonged *geta*, 'clogs,' or *zori*, 'sandals'.

tasuki A string or narrow band of material looped about the arms and across the shoulders to secure the long flowing sleeves of the kimono when one is working.

tatami needle A long, heavy needle used to sew the woven grass covering on to *tatami* mats, the thick rice straw mats used as floor covering.

tengu Mischievous ogres, not particularily malevolent but temperamental and easily angered. They are generally thought to be bright red with greatly elongated noses. They are sometimes winged, otherwise generally of human form.

toshigami Literally, "year deity." The deity to whom offerings of food are made at the close of the year to assure prosperity in the coming year.

ujigami A tutelary deity; the deity to whom a village shrine is dedicated.

Bibliography

AARNE, ANTTI. *Die magische Flucht: Eine Märchenstudie.* Helsinki: 1930.

——. *Die Tiere auf der Wanderschaft.* Hamina: 1913.

AARNE, ANTTI, and THOMPSON, STITH. *The Types of the Folktale.* Helsinki: 1961.

ASTON, W. E. (trans.). *Nihongi.* London: 1956.

BECK, HORACE P. *The Folklore of Maine.* Philadelphia and New York: 1957.

CHAMBERLAIN, BASIL HALL (trans.). *Kojiki.* Tokyo: 1906.

CHRISTIANSEN, REIDAR TH. *The Migratory Legends.* Helsinki: 1958.

COWELL, E. B. (ed.). *The Jātaka.* 6 vols. Cambridge: 1897.

COX, MARIAN ROALFE. *Cinderella.* London: 1893.

DORSON, RICHARD M. *Folk Legends of Japan.* Tokyo: 1961.

——. *Negro Folktales in Michigan.* Cambridge: 1956.

EBERHARD, WOLFRAM. *Typen Chinesischer Volksmärchen.* Helsinki: 1937.

HEARN, LAFCADIO. *Kwaidan.* New York and Boston: 1904.

IKEDA, HIROKO. "A Type and Motif Index of Japanese Folk-Literature." Unpublished Ph.D dissertation, Indiana University: 1955.

JONES, S. W. (trans.). *Ages Ago: Thirty-seven Tales from the Konjaku Monogatari.* Cambridge: 1959.

KEENE, DONALD (ed. and trans.). *The Old Woman, the Wife and the Archer.* New York: 1961.

KINOSHITA, JUNJI. *Yuzuru-Sankichi Banashi* (The Night Crane and Sankichi Tales). Tokyo: 1957.

KOHLER, JOSEF. *Der Ursprung der Melusinensage.* Leipzig: 1895.

MACKENSON, LUTZ. *Der singende Knochen*. Helsinki: 1923.

ROBERTS, WARREN E. *The Tale of the Kind and the Unkind Girls*. Berlin: 1958.

ROOTH, ANNA BIRGITTA. *The Cinderella Cycle*. Lund: 1951.

SEKI, KEIGO. *Nihon no Mukashi-banashi* (Japanese Folktales). 3 vols. Tokyo: 1956–57.

———. *Nihon Mukashi-banashi Shusei* (A Classification and Catalogue of Japanese Folktales). 6 vols. Tokyo: 1950–58.

THOMPSON, STITH. *The Folktale*. New York: 1946.

———. *Motif-Index of Folk Literature*, 6 vols. Bloomington, Ind. and Copenhagen: 1955–58.

THOMPSON, STITH, and BALYS, JONAS. *The Oral Tales of India*. Bloomington, Ind.: 1958.

THOMPSON, STITH, and ROBERTS, WARREN E. *Types of Indic Oral Tales*. Helsinki: 1960.

WILLAMS, C. A. S. *Encyclopedia of Chinese Symbolism and Art Motives*. New York: 1960.

ZONG, IN-SOB. *Folk Tales from Korea*. London: 1952.

Index of Motifs *

B. ANIMALS

Motif No.		Tale No.
B366	Animals grateful for release from captivity	31
B601.7	Marriage to monkey	47
B652.2	Man marries crane in human form	25

D. MAGIC

D361.1	The swan maiden	23
D475.1.1	Transformation: coals to gold	43
D612.1	Illusory transformations of animals in order to sell and cheat	31
D670	Magic flight	16
D672	Obstacle flight	19
D1110	Magic conveyances	16
D2011	Years thought days	32
D2063.5	Magic discomfort, continued breaking of wind	34

E. THE DEAD

E632.1	Speaking bones of murdered person reveal murder	42

F. MARVELS

F601	Extraordinary companions	18

H. TESTS

H310	Son-in-law tasks	23

J. THE WISE AND THE FOOLISH

J31	Encounter with clever children (woman) dissuades man from visit	51
J1250	Clever verbal retorts—general	61
J1500	Clever practical retort	62
J1675	Clever dealing with a king	57
J1795	Image in mirror mistaken for picture	55
J1805	Other misunderstandings of words	59
J1805.2	Unusual word misunderstood	60

K. DECEPTIONS

K511	Uriah letter changed	22
K561	Escape by persuading captor to talk	4
K891	Dupe tricked into jumping to his death	47

* From Stith Thompson, *Motif-Index of Folk Literature* (6 vols.; Bloomington, Ind., 1955–58).

Motif No. | | *Tale No.*

K1335   Seduction (or wooing) by stealing clothes of bathing girl (swan maiden)   23

L. REVERSAL OF FORTUNE

L101   Unpromising hero   24
L315.1   Bird flies into large animal's ear and kills him   8

N. CHANCE AND FATE

N271   Murder will out   42
N421.1   Progressive lucky bargains   50
N691.1   Numskull's outcry overawes tiger who is carrying him on his back   12

Q. REWARDS AND PUNISHMENTS

Q2   Kind and unkind   35
Q262   Impostor punished   34, 35

R. CAPTIVES AND FUGITIVES

R111.1.1   Rescue of princess from ogre   16

S. UNNATURAL CRUELTY

S411.2   Wife banished for some small fault   49, 50
S431   Castoff wife exposed in boat   49

T. SEX

T11.0.1   Marriage to supernatural wives who disappear   26
T125   Lazy boy and industrious girl matched   43
T543.3   Birth from a fruit   17

W. TRAITS OF CHARACTER

W152   Stinginess   58

X. HUMOR

X905   Lying contests   52
X1423.1   Lie: the great cabbage   52

Index of Tale Types *

I. ANIMAL TALES (1–299)

Type		Tale No.
1	The Theft of Fish	1
2	The Tail Fisher	1
3	Sham Blood and Brains	2
9	The Unjust Partner	5
43	The Bear Builds a House of Wood, the Fox of Ice	3
91	Monkey (Cat) Who Left His Heart at Home	11
123	The Wolf and the Kids	21
156	Thorn Removed from Lion's Paw (Androcles and the Lion)	7
210	Cock, Hen, Duck, Pin, and Needle on a Journey	5, 6
228	The Titmouse Tries To Be as Big as a Bear	8
275	The Race of the Fox and the Crayfish	9, 10

II. ORDINARY FOLKTALES
A. Tales of Magic (300–749)

Type		Tale No.
300	The Dragon Slayer	15
301	The Three Stolen Princesses	16, 18
303	The Twins or Blood Brothers	15
313	The Girl as Helper in the Hero's Flight	23, 24
314	The Youth Transformed to a Horse	24
326	The Magician and His Pupil	31
327A	Hänsel and Gretel	20
333	The Glutton (Red Ridinghood)	21
400	The Man on a Quest for His Lost Wife	23
403A	The Black and the White Bride	29
425	The Search for the Lost Husband	27
465	The Man Persecuted because of His Beautiful Wife	48
465A	The Quest for the Unknown	23
480	The Spinning Women by the Spring. The Kind and the Unkind Girls	33, 34, 35
503	The Gifts of the Little People	36, 37
510A	Cinderella	38
513A	Six Go through the Whole World	18
563	The Table, the Ass, and the Stick	39
565	The Magic Mill	39
671	The Three Languages	40
700	Tom Thumb	28
706	The Maiden without Hands	30

* From Antti: Aarne and Stith Thompson, *The Types of the Folktale* (Helsinki, 1961).

Type   *Tale No.*
707   The Three Golden Sons   49
736   Luck and Wealth   50

B. Religious Tales (750–849)

750B   Hospitality Rewarded   41
780   The Singing Bone   42
822   The Lazy Boy and the Industrious Girl   42
834A   The Pot of Gold and the Pot of Scorpions   44

C. Novelle (Romantic Tales) (850–999)

910G   Man Buys a Pennyworth of Wit   46
981   Wisdom of Hidden Old Man Saves Kingdom   53

III. JOKES AND ANECDOTES (1200–1999)

1462   The Unwilling Suitor Advised from Tree   54
1537   The Corpse Killed Five Times   56
1645A   Dream of Treasure Bought   45

IV. FORMULA TALES (2000–2399)

2031C   The Man Seeks the Greatest Being as a Husband
        for His Daughter   13
2300   Endless Tales   14

Index of Kata Numbers

II. ANIMAL TALES (31–74)

Kata No.		Tale No.
31	The Fish Thief	1
34A	The Badger, the Rabbit, and the Otter	2
36	The Quail and the Badger	4
41	The Mudsnail and the Fox	10
45	The Race of the Tiger and the Fox	9
49	The Wren as King of the Birds	8
50	The Hawk and the Wren	8
52B	Monkey Cheats Crab	5
53	The Battle of the Monkey and the Crab	6
61	The Monkey's Liver	11
70	The Mole's Bridegroom	13
72B	Kachi Kachi Mountain	3
73B	The Rabbit and the Bear	3
74	The Rain Leak in an Old House	12

III. MEN AND DEMONS (75–132)

Kata No.		Tale No.
75	The Three Lucky Charms	19
80	The Sky Deity's Golden Chain	21
82A, B	Kozuna, the *Oni*'s Child	16, 20
91A	Conquering the Monkey Demon	15
119	The Grateful Wolf	7
130	The Lucky Teakettle	31

IV. SUPERNATURAL HUSBANDS AND WIVES (133–150)

Kata No.		Tale No.
135	The Monkey Bridegroom	47
146	The Crane Wife	25
149	The Wife from the Upper World	23

V. SUPERNATURAL BIRTHS (151–165)

Kata No.		Tale No.
151	The Mudsnail Son	27
153	Issun Boshi, 'Little One Inch'	28
157	Riki-Taro, 'the Mighty Boy'	18
159	Momotaro, 'Peach Boy'	17

VI. HUMAN BEINGS AND WATERSPIRITS (166–170)

Kata No.		Tale No.
167	Urashima Taro	32
168	The Swamp Deity's Letter	22

VII. MAGIC OBJECTS (171–182)

Kata No.		Tale No.
171A	The Listening Hood	40
173	The Salt-Grinding Millstones	39

VIII. TALES OF FATE (183–188)

183B	The Charcoal Burner *Choja*	43

IX. MARRIAGE OF MEN AND OGRESSES (189–200)

189	The Wife's Portrait	48
195	The Gambler Son-in-law	54

X. FINDING TREASURES (201–209)

201	The Straw Rich Man	50
204	The Man Who Bought a Dream	45
207	Luck from Heaven and Luck from the Earth	44

XI. CONFLICTS (210–253)

210	Komebuku and Awabaku	38
211	Dish-Dish Mountain	38
213	The Girl without Arms	30
216	The Fire Boy	24
220	The White Bird Sister	29
223	The Skeleton's Song	42
236	The Old Man Who Caught Wild Ducks	35
238	The Old Man Who Cut Bamboo	34
239	The Tongue-cut Sparrow	33
241	The Old Men Who Had Wens	36
242	The Monkey Jizo	37

XII. TRICKSTERS (254–262)

259	Clever Yasohachi	56

XIV. CONTESTS (309–326)

315	The Boasting Match	52
316	The Child Who Told Tall Tales	51
320	The Precepts Bought for a Thousand *Ryo*	46

XV. PRIESTS AND ACOLYTES (327–344)

328	The Gold-Bearing Tree	49
329	The Mountain Where Old People Were Abandoned	53
332	A Razor Swims	62
333	The White Eggplant's Father	62
340	There's No Deity on the Priest's Head	61

Kata No.   *Tale No.*

341   Horse Dung   62
343   Bedding in One's Ear   63

XVII. FOOLISH PEOPLE (357-452)

366   The Snow Wife   26
380   Stinginess   58
392   Mis-hearing   59
416   The Nun's Arbitration   55

XVIII. FORMULA TALES (453-457)

457   Endless Tales   14

General Index

(References to headnotes are given in italics.)

Aarne, Antti (Finnish folklorist), *17*, *48*, *134*

Acolytes, *48*, 49, 51, 109, 162, 194–97

Adoption of husbands, *135*, 135

Aesop, *24*, 25

African tradition, *24*, 25, 92, *145*, *189*

Afterlife, 96, 97

Agari *choja*, 142–45, 151–53

Agawa-gun, *4*

Aichi-ken, *118*

Akita-ken, *47*

Amakusa-gun, *181*

American Indian tradition, *24*, 25, 92, *189*

American Negro tradition, *4*, 25, *145*

American tradition, *158*, *189*, 194

Ancestors, 153

Androcles, *21*

Anger, 6, 7, 13, 16, 20, 38, 45, 116, 120, 124, 153, 174, 180, 196, 197

Animals. *See* individual species

Anniversary of death, 70, 73, 74, 110, 111, 160

Aomori-ken, *81*

Apuleius, *82*

Arabian Nights, *176*

Arabic tradition, *126*, 160

Arai, Kikue (collector), *3*

Arthur, King, story of, *44*

Asakura, Toshizo (informant), 57

Asamai-mura, *47*

Ascetic, 58

Asian tradition, *17*, *24*, 25, 26, *131*, *135*

Aso-gun, *167*

Baboons, 36

Badgers, 5, *6*, 7–9, 21, *107*

bakemono, 34–36, 46, 47

Balys, Jonas. *See* Thompson, Stith, and Balys, Jonas

Banishment, 71, 90, *119*, *173*, 174, 175, 177

Basile, Giovanni Battista, 92

Bears, 4, *6*, 9–13, 21

Beck, Horace, 158

Beggars, 104

Benfey, Theodor (German folklorist), *107*

Benizara, 131–34

Bester, John, *184*

Biblical accounts, 57

Biwa, Lake, *182*, 183

Blacksmiths, 21

Boars, 22, 23

Breaking wind, *119*, 119, 120, 174, 175

Buddha birth stories, 26

Buddhist beliefs, 92, *176*

Buddhist legends, *135*

Buddhist myth, 57

Buddhist sermons, 29

Buddhist writings, *44*

Calves, 35

Carpenters, 154

Cats, 25, 116, 144

Charcoal burners, 153–55

Chaucer, Geoffrey, *14*, 22, *98*

Cheremis tradition, *119*

Chickens, 196

Childlessness, *82*, 83, 90

Children, sale of, *107*, 109, 110

Children's literature, 25, 29, *40*, 90, *107*, *111*, *115*, 120, *126*, *194*

Chinese tradition, *3, 17, 27, 33, 36, 40, 55, 99, 131, 135, 145, 155, 170, 184*

Cho, Kakuko (informant), *30*

Chobei, 4, 5

choja, 72, 82, 85–87, 89, 142–45, 151–53, *158*, 158–60

Christiansen, Reidar Th. (Norwegian folklorist), *158*

Cinderella cycle, *131*

Cleanliness, ritual, *64*, 69

Cleverness, 189–91; clever advice, 161, 162, 185; clever retorts, 195–97; clever youngest child, 52–54, 169

Closing formulas, 14, 29, 30, 36, 47, 125, *167*, 170, *170*, 173, 195

Cocks, *14*

Concubines, *170*

Covetousness, 59, 60, 86, 124, 125, 129, 130, 138

Cowell, E. B., *26*

Cows, 116

Cox, Marian Roalfe (English folklorist), *131*

Crabs, 16, 25

Cranes, 78–80, *112*, 114

Crucifixion, 148

Cruelty, 70, 94, 100, 107, 123

Cupid and Psyche, *82*

David and Bathsheba, *57*

Deceptions: disguises, 8, 55, 56, 72; false accusations, 174; hiding, 53, 133; imitating deity, 129, 187; lying, 26, 71, 94, 110, 146, 162, 195; misdirecting, 18; rewriting letters, 58, 59, 102, 103; shamming death, 3, 132; shamming drowning, 181; shamming forgetfulness, 74; shamming happiness, 172, 173; shamming healing, 181; shamming helpfulness, 189, 190; shamming kindness, 69, 99; shamming sickness, 5, 17; shamming weakness, 10; trickery, 4, 7, 11–15, 24, 25, 49, 50, 94, 169

Deities: of forest, 136; of harvest, 194; from heaven, 73, 74; on mountain, 34–36, 126; of road, 194; of sky, 57; of storehouse, 153; of the sun, 143; of thunder, 53; of undersea kingdom, 26; of water, 83–89, 195

Disguises. *See* Deceptions

Disney, Walt, *55*

Divination, 75

Divine punishment, fear of, 34, 35

Doctors, 83, 141

Dogs, 26, 35–39, *41*, 42, 43, 122–24, 144

dondo harai, 20, 195

dondo hare, 47

Dorson, Richard M. (American folklorist), *21, 57, 63, 77, 118, 121, 145, 151, 158, 181*

dotto harai, 14

Dragon kingdom. *See* Neinya

Dragon slaying, *33*

Dreams, 152, *155*, 156, 157, *158*, 158, 159, 162

Eagle, 22

Eastern European tradition, *155*, 170

Eat-Sleep, 186

Eberhard, Wolfram (folklorist and sociologist), *17, 27, 36, 55, 155, 184*

Echigo province, 159, 160

Edda, *63*

Edo, *70*, 70, 71, 99, 101–4

Emperor, 22, *44*, 91

Endless tales, *30*

Enuma-gun, *115*

Esashi-gun, *57*, 128

Etiological ending, 6, 14–16, 23, 27–30, 51, 57, 60, 69, 114, 138, 145, 155

European peasants, *151*

European tradition, *3*, *14*, *17*, *24*, *25*, *26*, *27*, *30*, *36*, *40*, *44*, *51*, *90*, *92*, *98*, *99*, *107*, *126*, *131*, *135*, *142*, *158*, *167*, *173*, *176*, *181*, *184*, *189*

Fabliau, *189*
Farmers, 7, 82–87, *185*
Farming, 17, 18, 156
Fate, bestowing of, 152
Festivals, 33, 87, 88, 99, 100. *See also* Harvest festivals
Fish, 3, 112, 113
Fishermen, 3, 112, 113
Flies, 50
Foxes, 3, *14*, 25, *107*, 107–11
French tradition, *33*
Fudoki (eighth-century collection of local records), *63*
Fuji, Mt., 58
Fujii, Tetsuya (informant), *139*
Fujisaki-mura, *81*
Fukuoka-mura, *128*
Fukusawa, Shichiro, *184*
Furukawa, Takeo (informant), *16*
Furuyashiki, Yonezo (informant), *107*

Gifu-ken, *195*
Goats, 144
Gombei, 170–73
Goro, 153–55
Gosen-mura, *170*
Grave offerings, 155
Greed, 118, 120, 123
Greek mythology, *139*
Guntram, King, legend of, *158*

Hachi-no-Ki (Noh drama), *142*
Hagoromo (Noh drama), *63*
Hamamatsu City, *130*
Haneishi, Tanie (informant), *126*, *134*, *145*
Hare, *4*, 5, *6*, 23, 25. *See also* Rabbits
Harvest festivals, 21, 153, 155
Hata-gun, *197*

Hawks, 23, 191
Healing, magic, 142
Hearn, Lafcadio, *81*, *111*, *112*
Heaven, 64, 65, 73, 87
Hienuki-gun, *16*, *98*
Higashi Iyayamamura, *54*
Higo province, 182, 183
Hikoichi, *190*
Hikoichi-Kichiyomu cycle, *190*, *192*
Hiraka-gun, *47*
Hirano, Kura (informant), *6*
Hirano, Ushinosuka (informant), *43*
Hirata, Shiza (informant), *195*
Hitabayashi, Mitsue (collector), *90*
Homer, 57
Honma, Teki (informant), *170*
Horse drivers, 84
Horseflies, *158*
Horses, 27, 28, 57, 72–74, 76, 84, 110, 111, 116
Hospitality, 143
Hungarian tradition, *30*

ichigo buranto kudatta, *173*
Iida-mura, *21*, *183*
Ikeda, Hiroko (Japanese folklorist), *14*, *15*, *16*, *24*, 25, 27, 29, *36*, *99*, *118*, *120*, *131*, *145*, *151*, *167*, *170*, *174*, *176*
Ikkyu-san, *194*
Iliad, 57
Imitation, unsuccessful, 57, 120, 125, 130, 134
Indian tradition, *3*, *14*, *17*, *26*, *29*, *33*, *44*, *92*, *99*, *107*, *131*, *135*, *139*, *155*, *160*, *161* 170, *173*, *181*, *183*, *184*, *186*
Indochinese tradition, *181*
Indonesian tradition, 25
Inhospitality, 143
Iri *choja*, 142–45, 151–53
Irish tradition, *126*
Iruma-gun, *3*, *90*
Irving, Washington, *112*
Isawa-gun, 22

Ise, 57-59, *112*, 114
Ise, Grand Shrines of, *57*
Ishihara, Jiro (informant), *160*
Ishikawa-ken, *115*
Ishikotaro, 'Rock Boy,' 45-47
Isshaya City, *15*
Italian tradition, *126*
Iwasaki, Kigomi (collector), *21*
Iwate-gun, 6
Iwate-ken, *6*, *16*, *22*, *43*, *57*, *82*, *98*, *107*, *126*, *128*, *134*, *145*, *193*, *194*
Izanami (mythological creator), *47*, *48*

Jātaka, *26*, *139*
Jealousy, 59, *102*, *174*
Jellyfish, 140
Jimmu (legendary emperor), *44*
Jiro, *121*, 121
Jizo-*sama*, *129*, 129, 130, 195
Jones, S. W., *26*
Judges, *145*

Kabuki drama, *131*, *184*
Kagawa-ken, *111*
Kagoshima-ken, *25*, *63*, *70*, *77*, *92*, *139*, *142*, *151*, *160*, *176*, *179*
Kakeroma Island, *63*
Kakezara, 131-34
Kamakura period, *142*
Kameishi highway, 45
kami, *151*, *194*, 195
Kami Kuishiki-mura, *51*, *186*
Kami Mashiki-gun, *30*
Kami Niikawa-gun, *120*
Kami Shichibe, 146-48
kamidana, 83-85, *187*
Kamihei-gun, *82*, *107*, *125*, *134*, *145*, *193*
Kana, 94, 98
Kanashi, King, *178*
Kaniharu, 93-97
Kannon (goddess of mercy), *91*
Karoku, 78-80
katattemo kataraidemo sooroo, 125
Kawai, Yutaro (collector), *81*

Kawauchi, Mitsu (informant), *4*
Keene, Donald, *184*
Kichiyomu, *190*, 192
Kikai Island, *25*
Kikuchi, Masuji (informant), *128*
Kindness, 100, 136, 137, 146, *184*; to animals, 78, 108, 115, 116, 122, 139
Kings, 22, *96*, 97, *176*, 179
Kinoshita, Junji (playwright), 77, *170*, *186*, *190*
Kitamae Oshima, 112
Kitashidara-gun, *118*
Kitataki-gun, *15*
Kites, 191
kobito, 136, 137
Kochi-ken, *4*, *190*, *197*
Kohama, 24
Kohama, Taichi (informant), 27
Kohler, Josef (German folklorist), *78*
Kojiki (eighth-century historical record), *33*, *44*, *47*, *63*
Konbitaro, 'Dirt Boy,' 44-47
konde oshimae, 36
Konjaku Monogatori (eleventh-century tale collection), *26*, *176*, *183*
Kono, Kesa (informant), *186*
Kono, Tsume (informant), *51*
Korean tradition, 27, *55*, *129*, *189*
Koreichi, *191*, 191
Koshiki Island, *160*
Krohn, Kaarle (Finnish folklorist), *3*
Kuma-gun, 27
Kumamoto-ken, *14*, 27, *30*, *167*, *181*
Kurokawa-mura, *167*
Kuzumaki-mura, 29, *36*, *158*, *189*
Kyoto, *90*

Lions, *21*, 25
Lords, *14*, 14, 15, 100-102, 104, *111*, 119-20, 133-34, 141, 147-48, *172*, 174-75, 184-85, *189*
Love sickness, 74, 75, *171*

Lucky exchange, 177–79
Lying. *See* Deceptions

Mabinogion, 44
Mackenson, Lutz (German folklor-
    ist), 145
Mackerel, 181
Magic objects: ashes, 121, 125; bam-
    boo tree, 66, 67; boat, 80; box,
    114, 132; charms, 48, 49; con-
    veyances, 39; ear, 140, 141;
    flowers, 38; flying robe, 64–66;
    gold-producing horse, 59, 60;
    gold-producing mill, 124; leaf,
    143; mill, 134, 137, 138; mortar
    and pestle, 121; mulberries, 76;
    rice, 143; screen, 178; sword,
    178; table, ass, and stick, 135;
    thousand-league boots, 53; trans-
    forming powders, 144; water of
    life, 76, 77; wish-fulfilling ham-
    mer, 90, 91, 92
Magojiro, 57–59
Makino, Etsu (informant), 29, 36,
    158, 189
Mamichigane, 70–77
Man of Law's Tale, The, 98
Manyoshu (ninth-century poem col-
    lection), 63
Marriage: with animals, 167, 167–
    69; with supernatural beings, 65,
    81; with transformed animals,
    79, 86, 87
Marriage, request for, from woman
    who has sought shelter, 78, 79,
    81, 154, 171
Medieval exempla, 151, 160
Melampus, 139
Melusina myth, 78
Merchants, 89, 158
Messengers, 101–3
Mice, 29, 54, 144
Midokotaro, 'Red Temple Boy,' 45–
    47
Midwife, 83
Mikeran, 64–69

Mima-gun, 54
Minami Kanbara-gun, 29, 36, 155,
    158, 189
Minami Tsugaru-gun, 81
Minami Uonuma-gun, 192
Mino province, 182, 183
Mirrors, 112, 114, 188
Misunderstanding, 13, 193, 194
Mitsuke-mura, 155
Miyagi-ken, 33
Miyama Daigonken Temple, 45
Mizouke swamp, 57
Mizusawa-mura, 22
mochi, pounding of, 18
Moles, 29, 29, 30
Monkey-crab battle cycle, 15, 16, 17
Monkeys, 5, 6, 16–20, 26, 28, 36,
    42, 43, 144, 145, 167, 167–70
Momotaro, 'Peach Boy,' 41–43
Mongolian tradition, 14, 107
Mono-gun, 33
Moral ending, 118, 125, 126
Mori, 24
Moriguchi, Tari (collector), 22
Muju (monk), 29
Murder, 146
Mutilation, 100

Nagahama, 34–36
Nagano-ken, 21, 183
Nagasaki, 30
Nagasaki-ken, 15
Naha City, 176
Naka Kanbara-gun, 170
Nakagawa, Kin (informant), 173
Nakano, Kozo (informant), 54
Nakatado-gun, 111
Narito, Matsu (informant), 192
Naze City, 139
Near Eastern tradition, 115, 161
Neinya, 26, 113, 139, 140, 152
Neriya. *See* Neinya
Nibukawa-mura, 195
Nihongi (eighth-century historical
    record), 22, 111, 170

Niigata-ken, 29, 36, 155, 158, 170,
    173, 189, 192
Ninohei-gun, 194
Nintoku, Emperor, 22
Nira. See Neinya
Nishi Yatsushiro-gun, 51, 186
Nishitani-mura, 115
Noblemen. See Lords
Nobori, Shomu (informant), 63
Noh drama, 63, 142
Norse mythology, 139
North Carolina, tradition in, 119
Norwegian tradition, 158, 186
Nun's Priest's Tale, 14
nushi, 57, 58

Obligations, repayment of, 40
Obscene gestures, 6, 7, 39, 40
Octopus, 26, 27, 140
Odashima, Sada (informant), 98
Ogasawara, Kinzo (informant), 82
Ogres, 51
Ogress, 48, 58
Oita-ken, 192
Okierabu Island, 70, 92, 142, 151,
    176
Okinawa, 174, 176
Okuninushi (mythological charac-
    ter), 63
One-Stick-of-Bamboo, 153, 155
oni, 37–39, 40, 42, 43, 52–54, 91,
    132
Oni Island, 42, 43
oni woman, 48–51
Ono-gun, 195
Ooka Echizen-no-Kami, 145
Oose, 180
Oriental tradition, 33, 155, 160
Orito, Kenso (collector), 15
Osawa (castle town), 46
Oshima-gun, 23, 25, 63, 70, 92, 139,
    142, 151, 176
Ota, Eitaro (collector), 120
Ota-mura, 120
Otters, 5

Oumi province, 34–46
Ozuya-mura, 194

Pantschantantra, 107
Paradise, 111
Parlement of Foules, 22
Peddlers, 4, 154, 175, 181
Pentamerone, 92
Persian tradition, 160
Pheasants, 17, 17–20, 22, 42, 43
Pilgrimage, 57, 57–59
Poverty, 78, 83, 107, 151, 153, 154,
    161, 186, 197
Prayer, 57, 83, 85, 88, 126
Pregnancy, 38, 83, 151
Priest-acolyte cycle, 194, 195, 197
Priestess, 37–40, 75
Priests, 26, 33–36, 48, 50, 51, 108,
    109, 143–45, 162, 194–97
Princess, 113, 114
Prostitution, 107, 109, 110
Proverbs, 23, 186
Punishment: by beating, 27; by
    crucifixion, 148; by death, 20, 57,
    58, 98, 118, 134; by deprivation,
    155, 157; by drowning, 12, 138,
    180; by humiliation, 123, 124,
    128, 130, 173; by mutilation, 15,
    120; threat of, 35; by transforma-
    tion into animals, 144; unspeci-
    fied, 104, 129
Puppy, 122
Pursuit, 39, 49, 50, 54, 56

Rabbits, 6, 9–13, 24. See also Hare
Rain-Leak-in-an-Old-House, 28
Ramayana, 139
Ranke, Kurt (German folklorist),
    33
Rats, 29, 30
Rejuvenation, 144
Renaissance jestbooks, 151, 160
Resuscitation, 77
Reunion, 175, 179
Rewards, nature of: articles to sell,
    108, 109, 111; entertainment, 113,

140; food, 22; gifts, 120, 190; marriage to daughters, 47, 142; money, 118, 122, 125, 129, 157, 163; restoration of physical well-being, 127, 144; treasure, 43, 79, 140

Rewards, reasons for: bravery, 43; cleverness, 163, 190; deliverance, 47, 79, 108–10, 139, 142; entertainment, 120, 125, 127; kindness, 22, 113, 118, 144, 157

Reynard the Fox cycle, 3, 4, 6

Rice tax, yearly, 83–85

Rip Van Winkle, 111

Riverbear bird, 23

Roberts, Warren E. (American folklorist), 115, 118, 120. See also Thompson, Stith, and Roberts, Warren E.

rokubu. See Ascetic

Rooth, Anna Birgitta (Swedish folklorist), 131

Russian tradition, 119

Ryoi-ki (ninth-century literary work), 170

Ryugu. See Neinya

Sacrifice, human, 34–36, 46

Sado Island, 158, 159, 173

Saga, Lord, 93, 94, 96–98

St. Germanus, legend of, 142

Saitama-ken, 3, 90

Samurai, 92, 125

Sangoku Denki, 170

Sanya choja, 158

Saraki-mura, 6, 43

Sasaki, Hiroyuki (collector), 118

Saseki-Shu (thirteenth-century collection), 29

Sashi, Kubomori (informant), 70, 92, 142, 151, 176

Sashu, 92

Sashu, Lord, 92–94, 98

Saso-gun, 14

Sato, Genji (informant), 194

Satsuma-gun, 77, 160, 179

Satsuma province, 30, 182, 183

Sayagi Island, 111

Scandinavian mythology, 142

Scandinavian tradition, 158

Sea bream, 112, 139

Sea slug, 24

Selfishness, 136, 143

Sennin Nagane (mountain pass), 45

Shams. See Deceptions

Shimizu-mura, 4

Shimo Shichibe, 146–48

Shimoda, 24

Shimoina-gun, 21, 183

shimyaa, 29

Shinto, 57, 112

Shippei Taro, 33, 34–36

Shizuoka-ken, 130

Shogunate, 70, 99

Shrines, 34, 35, 57, 58, 75, 83, 89, 90, 104, 112, 126, 129, 151, 187

Shumi Mountain, 179, 180

Siberian tradition, 173

Siegfried, 139

Skeletons, 147, 148

Snails, 82, 83–89

Snake goddess, 57

Snakes, 141, 142, 157

Sogi (fifteenth-century poet and priest), 179

Solomon, King, 184

Soul, 92, 96, 97, 176

Sparrows, 115–18, 140

Spined swellfish, 26, 27

Stealing, 116, 138

Stepmother, evil, 51, 70, 70, 71, 93, 98, 99, 102, 104, 131, 131, 133

Stinginess, 192

Storytellers, professional, 167

Stupidity, 4, 10–12, 193

Sugawara, Keisuke (collector), 33

Suicide, 89, 155

Sumiyoshi-sama, 90

Sun Goddess, 33

Supernatural birth: from dirt, 44; from peaches, 41, 41, 122; as tiny child, 83, 90

Supernatural bridegroom, *82*, 87
Supernatural growth, 41, 44, 92
Supernatural healing, 103, 127, 142
Supernatural helper: wife, 68, 69; flying horse, 72, 73
Supernatural strength, 44, 45
Supernatural wife, 65–69, 79, 81
Susanowo (brother of the Sun Goddess), *33*
Suzuki, Kiyomi (collector), *183*
Swamp *nushi. See nushi*
Sweetfish, 195
Sydow, Carl von, Swedish folklorist, 142

Taka swamp, 58
Takaoka-gun, *190*
Tall tales, *181*, 182, *183*
Tama-no-Chu, 93, 94, 98
Tanabata festival, *63*
Tanba province, *111*
Tanka poetry, *131*
Taro, *121*, 121
Tasks, difficult or unusual, 67–69, *115*, 116, 117, 133
Temple, 34, 36–38, 45, 108, 136, 162, 197
tengu, 127, 128
Terada, Denichiro (collector), *47*
Teradomari village, 158
Thieves, 27
Thompson, Stith (American folklorist), *3*, *24*, *25*, *29*, *30*, *33*, *43*, *51*, *90*, *92*, *98*, *107*, *126*, *134*, *139*, *142*, *160*, *173*, *176*, *181*, *184*, *189*
Thompson, Stith, and Balys, Jonas, 27
Thompson, Stith, and Roberts, Warren E., *3*, *17*, *26*, *29*, *33*, *44*, *115*, *184*
Thor, 142
Thousand and One Nights, The, *63*
Three Little Pigs, The, 55
Tiger, 25
Tiger-wolf, 27, 28

Tit, 119
Tokamachi-mura, *192*
Tokorozawa-mura, *90*
Tokushima-ken, *54*
Tomi, Saneyoshi (informant), *25*
Tomioka-mura, *3*
Tono-mura, *82*
Tortoise, 23, 25
Toyama-ken, *120*
Toyone-mura, *118*
Transformations: bird into girl, 97, 98; children into dogs, 144; crane into woman, 78; fox into girl, 109, 110; fox into horse, 110; fox into teakettle, 108; girl into bird, 95; man and wife into monkeys, 144; man into crane, *112*, 114; servants into animals, 144; snail into man, 89; sword into snake, 178
Trapping, of animals, 7
Treasure, finding of, 154, 156, *158*, 159, 160
Trickery. *See* Deceptions
Trickster, *4*
Tsuchibuchi-mura, *107*, *126*, *134*, *145*
Turtle, 112–14

Uji Shui (thirteenth-century collection), *126*, *176*, *186*
ujigami, 187
Unselfishness, 117
Urashima Taro, 112–14
Ushinichi plains, 153
Ushirogawa-mura, *197*

Wada, Sotaro (informant), *111*
Waga-gun, *6*, *43*, *44*
Waka poetry. *See* Tanka poetry
Watanabe, Hana (collector), *130*
Whales, 24
Williams, C. A. S., *40*
Wolves, 21, 21, 22, 132, 133
Worship, 73, 74, 88
Wrens, 22

Yagi, Sanji (collector), *167*
Yakushi-*sama*, 87–89
Yamada Muchi Nuyashi, 93
Yamaguchi-ken, *23*
Yamanashi-ken, *51, 186*
Yamashita, Hisao (collector), *115*
Yamashita, Isamu (informant), *181*
yamauba, 55, 55–57
Yazawa-mura, *16, 98*

Year's end meal, *135,* 136, 137, 142, 143
Yonesato-mura, *57*
Yoshii, Motozo (informant), *155*
Yunomae-mura, *27*
Yura, 24
Yusuharu-mura, *190*

Zong, In-sob (Korean folklorist), *55, 129, 189*